Simple Physics

Simple Physics

or
Go, Go, Galileo
or
Newton; Go Fig
or
Albert Einstein is a Big Fat Idiot
or
One Easy Piece
or
The Briefest History of Time

James M. Jacobs

Epigraph Publishing Service

Rhinebeck, NY

Printed in the United States of America

Library of Congress Control Number: 2014946173

ISBN: 978-1-936940-93-6

Book and cover design by Chris Hallman

Edited By Michelle C. Bruss

Epigraph Publishing Service
www.epigraphps.com
22 East Market Street, Suite 304
Rhinebeck, NY 12572

About the Author

James Michael Jacobs grew up in Oconomowoc, Wisconsin. (If the thought of pronouncing that name is too tiresome, you had better try another book.) He had a happy, "normal" childhood: playing army and catching frogs. He attended high school in Freeport, Illinois. It proved to be just that. His first experience with L.S.D. was highlighted (no pun intended) by a late night chat in the bedroom of his parents. It closed with "Do you want me to turn the lights out?" "Jim, the lights are out." "OK, good night."

The author excelled in high school. He played the lead in the school musical. James was elected student body president and named to the all-conference debate and golf teams. He dropped out of physics after the first day because it was too difficult.

The summer after his senior year, he climbed Longs' Peak in Colorado the hard way (from the south). He made the decent high on Blue Blazes acid (at the height of the Pleiades meteor shower) and his search for the truth began in earnest. The year was 1972.

He enrolled at the University of Ill(inois) in the fall. It proved to be just that. When he announced his intention to "find the truth" his intellectual college buddies dismissed him as "sophomoric" (as a mere freshman they evidently felt he was ahead of his time). Not to be dissuaded, he enrolled in a course named "Physics for Poets", which familiarized him with the history of physics. He also began to listen to music of the Grateful Dead. He completed a paper on the relationship between light and darkness.

At that time, he experienced a "cosmic awakening". He was later diagnosed as paranoid schizophrenic—though you wouldn't know it to meet him. He left on a trip to "speak with the dead". To his disappointment, he was told by Bob Weir a.k.a. "Ace" (rhythm guitar player for the "Dead"), "I believe in science." This took his search for the truth in a different direction. He began to read the Bible.

The author left the university with 59 credit hours in Liberal Arts and Sciences, a perennial sophomore. He began to study the Bible with Jehovah's Witnesses (also known as "the Truth" 3 John 3, 4) and was baptized on April 20, 1975. For the next 30 years, he continued to study the Bible. He served as a full-time minister, and was appointed as an elder at age 27. He was the youngest elder at the Watchtower Farms, where he spent nearly five years. ("Young elder". Yes, for a time James was a living oxymoron, which wasn't easy.) On October 25, 1986 he was married. A son was born the next year.

James was deleted as an elder when he was diagnosed with bipolar disorder in 1998 (compare 2 Chron 5:9; 1 Kings 8:8) (see Afterward). He had begun writing

Simple Physics earlier that year. Born October 5, 1954 (Libra/Balance) he has since been disfellowshipped for smoking (although the unstated grounds was apostasy). He hopes you find this little book "light" reading (Eccl 2:14). The heavy stuff is yet to come (compare Jn 16:12) (see Supplement).

To Yahowah, Yahshua, and Karyne.,
my three favorite persons.

Dedications

To Robin:

He could make me laugh, but couldn't fly.

To Debbie Carmichael

"Five sparrows sell for two coins of small value, do they not? Yet not one of them goes forgotten before God. Have no fear, you are worth more than many sparrows" (Luke 12:6, 7).

"And no more will my chieftains maltreat my people… That is enough of you, O chieftains of Israel" (Ezekiel 45:8, 9).

To Paxson Conners

For "…a word spoken at the right time for it" (Proverbs 25:11).

To Edwin "Ether" Herr

You don't see him coming, but he'll knock you out. He's invisible, yet everywhere, M.I.A.

To the humble, honest, hungry people of China

"But many that are first will be last and the last first" (Matthew 19:30).

Contents

Foreword

An older brother (Jehovah's Witnesses call their spiritual family "brothers" and "sisters") recently called into question my motives in publishing this book, as well as my qualifications (compare 1 Sam. 17:26-30). All I can do in answer is show you what I've got. He did, however, raise a valid question. He said, "Since modern scientists were able to fabricate an atomic bomb, doesn't that prove they know far more about physics than you do?"

Does the bomb blow up *Simple Physics*? No, it rather confirms it. Quantum mechanics did not build the bomb, men did. Those suppositions were basically false and yet they were able to build the bomb. How? How does nature build anything complex and orderly, from a single ant to the solar system? From the glassy reflective surface of the moon, to the transformation of a worm into a butterfly? The list goes on...and on...and on some more. How did these miracles happen? By accident, pure, unadulterated chance. The boys got lucky. The bomb was another dazzling accident of evolution. It required no intelligent direction whatsoever since it was destined to happen anyway. To this day, they don't really know what is taking place inside an atom bomb. At the time of its first testing, they didn't know if the device would incinerate the whole world (and they still don't). But raw evolution prevailed again. Those idiots lucked out and showed themselves evolutionarily superior to the sub-humans they were destined to destroy.

Should a bomb vindicate the validity of an idea? "Yes-we-know-we're-right-and-can-blow-you-up-to-prove-it." That doesn't really meet the test of evidence. Modern physics can overawe us with their sophisticated weaponry. An example from history did similarly. Goliath of Gath had a spear with a shaft like the beam of loom workers and a blade of iron weighing fifteen pounds (1 Sam 17:7). When they had a contest, David ran out to him with five smooth stones, but not just any smooth stones. They were the "five smoothest stones from the torrent valley" (1 Sam 17:40). That means they were provided by God, not found by luck. The first of those simple stones dropped Goliath right on his face. This little book has five chapters. Just the first, entitled "Darkness," will administer a prefrontal lobotomy to Big Science. It will make a profound impression on their collective mind. The chapters that follow will use the giant's own weapons to take his head clean off. Or so the story goes. The contest is on. This little book is controversial. It is like David's sling. You, the reader, be a witness, and judge for yourself who comes off victorious. God knows we've all been standing on the sideline listening to this big mouth long enough (1 Sam 17:3, 16).

Post-Foreword

This is my little contribution to literary structure, the post-forward. Although it precedes the body of this little book, it's being written last, like yin and yang. In fact, that's what it's about. *Simple Physics* is the first successful effort at synthesizing Eastern and Western thought. The result is an appreciation of Qi or what I call force—both from an Eastern and Western standpoint. Simple Physics expresses Qi as $f/\emptyset$ or force over (universal) time. Qi is the fundamental concept of Chinese ideology, the very underpinning of yin/yang. This little book takes these thoughts full circle, so to speak. Are you starting to perceive the irony in all of this? You should, if you give me the honor of reading what follows. That sincere invitation is why I'm writing this last, but it is with a warning: The American Heritage Dictionary gives this third definition and example for the word ironic; "poignantly contrary to what is expected or intended: Madness, an ironic fate for such a clear thinker." My fervent prayer is that you the reader will share in my madness and enjoy it as much as I do. It is indeed, a beautiful thing (Compare Eccl 1: 17, 18; 2:12, 13).

Christmas morning 2005

Introduction

"He is revealing the deep things and the concealed things, knowing what is in the darkness, and with him the light does dwell." —Daniel 2:22

"Only two things are infinite, the universe and human stupidity, and I'm not sure about the former."
—Albert Einstein

"Your theory sounds crazy to me, young man. The question is: Is it crazy enough?" —Niels Bohr

Definition: Crazy—full of crazes (tiny cracks).

A few years ago, I was sharing some of my observations on physics and religion with my eleven-year-old son. I explained to him how, according to the Bible, Jehovah can measure the universe with the span of his hand (Isaiah 40:12). I told Zachary what that meant is that, to Jehovah, the universe is like a hardball. Without skipping a beat, he corrected, "No dad, it's like a softball." "A softball?

Why do you say that?" His reply? "Because Jehovah has big hands." That made me think (2 Chron 6:18).

This little book is written in hopes that you too will think about what I call Simple Physics. By doing so, you may learn more about God than that he has big hands. Why? Because..."his invisible qualities are clearly seen from the world's creation onward, because they are perceived by the things made, even his eternal power and Godship" (Rom 1:20). By perceiving those things made we will see evidence not only of eternal power, but of the Creator's Godship, the kind of God he is.

Chapter 1: Darkness

Several scientists are presently engaged in the search for what they call "dark matter."[1] They speculate that some 90% of the universe's mass consists of something yet undetected.[2] The implications of this were explained recently by Stephen Hawking on his PBS program Stephen Hawking's Universe (who died and made him God?) (Ps. 115:16). To paraphrase Mr. Hawking, "either we will find dark matter, meaning it's gravitational pull will collapse the universe into a big crunch, or we shall not find dark matter, meaning the universe shall continue expanding until it dissipates into a uniformly cold waste. Either way, it won't happen for 8-10 billion years, so I'm not too concerned. Ha, Ha." What Hawking failed to consider was a third scenario: that scientists continue on with their meaningless search as the universe continues eternally without them.

According to the Bible (Ps. 104:5 and Ps. 148:1-6) both the earth and the heavens will continue forever. How can this be possible? The Creator has arranged for it. For example, for life to continue on the earth, fresh water is needed. When God provided the earth as a home, he stocked it with a limited amount of fresh water. He then did something not easy to appreciate: He left the water running. It all runs into the ocean, water that we can't drink! Yet Solomon recognized even years ago that this is part of a cycle. God recycles and conserves limited resources. He doesn't waste a drop of this life-sustaining fluid (Eccl 1:7, Isa. 55:9-11). But look up! What's going on? What's God thinking? He left all the lights on! Before we start scolding, we would do well to remember the fact that God does not waste, but utilizes fully (compare Luke 9:17). His power is eternal (Romans 1:20). God cares about the stars that light the sky. Each one has a name (Ps. 147:4). They are numbered (Isa. 40:26, Ps. 147:4, Gen. 22:17) and they are unique (1 Cor. 15:41). The photons they (including the sun) radiate provide us with essential energy. What of those photons that fail to encounter matter or are reflected off of it? Are they wasted? The answer has to do with darkness.

Science defines darkness as the absence of light (first posited by Einstein). That doesn't sound like it amounts to a whole lot. This arbitrary and capricious definition is a major roadblock to understanding the physical universe. According to the Bible, darkness is a created thing. "Forming light and creating darkness…I, Jehovah, am doing all these things" (Isa 45:7). "Jehovah then said to Moses: 'Stretch your hand out towards the heavens, that darkness may occur over the land of Egypt and the darkness may be felt'" (Ex10:21). Much of Simple

Physics is based on a different definition of darkness.[3] Rather than being the absence of light, **darkness is the opposite of light**.[4] This basic truth is the crux of Simple Physics (Crux Simplex).[5] What does this imply?

First consider light. Light appears to be an extremely small particle that moves as a wave. Generally, light moves very quickly, though it has been reduced in speed to as little as 34 mph. It seems impossible, however, to stop its motion completely.

So what would the opposite of a particle constantly moving as a wave be? A vast field, by nature still, and able to transmit waves. This presents a picture of our existing in a vast ocean of darkness (see appendix A). The darkness is by nature still.

Picture yourself in a room with one window. Sunlight is streaming in. You can see every detail in the room. Now someone shutters the window. Suddenly you are immersed in the darkness—only not really. What is gone is the light. The darkness was always there. You were simply seeing the light. With the light gone, you are seeing the darkness (Jude 13) that was always there, still, cold, silent, extending through and beyond the walls to fill all of space: A vast ocean, strangely solid, through which light (matter) moves via crazes.[6] The two never touch (2 Cor. 6:14), yet are never apart.

Darkness constitutes what we call outer space. However, it is not simply an undifferentiated, homogenous ocean (see appendix A). Einstein postulated that space could be curved.[7] He did not really define what space is.[8] Any definitions of space should address the entropy problem, namely, how is order arrived at and maintained in a universe that tends toward disorder? The answer has to do with "doesn't matter." The sea of darkness we call outer space is crazed by countless tiny cracks of nothing called "doesn't matter." These crazes are in perfectly uniform arrangement throughout darkness (can you get any more crazy than that, Mr. Bohr?). When the Bible says the heavens are "like a fine gauze" (Isa. 40:22) it means like a really fine gauze-like structure. By means of this meshwork all space and its contents may be measured (Job 38:5, Ps. 19:4a). The presence of matter within this arrangement affects both the matter and the matrix we call outer space. It moves the darkness as it distorts the uniform arrangement of "doesn't matter." It is this bilateral (two-part) arrangement (entropy-driven matter within a super-structured field of darkness (outer space)) that results in a marriage of the two extremes: variety.[9] The presence of a superstructured field also accounts for the uniformity of the light waves it transmits.[10] Such waves occupy crazes. Darkness is the only field there is. It is a unified field.[11] It's the only game in town. Every painting has a background. Every flower has a field in which it is planted. The picture is incomplete without it. It's unnatural. In the same way the stars cannot exist except in a field of darkness. Darkness is the arrangement by which they are held in their assigned orbits (Judges 5:20, Jude 13). It's as though the stars were climbers, chimneying (or pushing out) among great columns of rock, held suspended in a vast ocean of darkness, moving. Simple Physics (2 Cor. 6:14).

The above-cited scripture reads, "What sharing does light have with darkness?" If they have no sharing, they have nothing in common. If they have nothing in common, they are exact opposites. **Darkness is the opposite of light.** If you can appreciate that statement, you'll make sense of all of Simple Physics. I call it the Crux Simplex or the "simple cross" (Latin). The crux is the basic, central or critical point or feature. It is at sharp variance with "darkness is the absence of light," which doesn't define darkness as anything. However, darkness is a thing, everything light isn't. Unlike light, darkness is not matter, it is "something nonexistent" (Isa. 40:17), antimatter. This is why scientists cannot find it. They are looking for dark matter. Darkness is not matter but can be found anywhere. It strikes me as humorous that these diligent scientists don miner's hats to go miles down mine shafts to conduct experiments on gravity and never ask: "Hey, what is all this stuff? Wait, that's simple. Everyone knows that's just darkness, common as dirt for God's sake. Better turn my lamp back on so I can see something."

What do you think causes light to move as a distinct wave? Light is causing a distortion in a superstructured field, a unified field: darkness. Isn't that some kind of proof or something—proof that such a field exists? According to Insight on the Scriptures Vol. 2 page 253 under "Light": "Light is the opposite of darkness, literally and figuratively." Conversely, darkness would be the opposite of light. This reference has no entry under "darkness" as a Bible term or subject, even though the Bible refers to it as early as Gen. 1:2 and throughout. Darkness is not to be feared, but is very good (see appendix E). It was created by God (Isa. 45:7). Light has no "sharing" with darkness (2 Cor. 6:14). This means they have nothing in common, which makes them opposites. One of the things they do not share is space. Darkness only exists where light does not. Light occupies its own space, within a "vast watery deep" of darkness: the "abyss" (Rom. 10:7) (see appendix A). This watery deep has a "boundary" (Job 38:20). It can be "felt" (Ex 10:21). The darkness might just as well be the light (Ps. 139:12) or ftn lit: "like the darkness, like the light." This is the case because darkness is light; antilight or antimatter. Darkness is the background for creation, the canvas that makes the painting possible. You might as well stop calling it the absence of light or you'll never figure the puzzle out. Just because darkness is something nonexistent doesn't mean it is not a reality. Darkness is all around us, so we might as well get comfortable with it. It's cool.

Chapter 2: Gravity

The cornerstone of Newtonian Physics is gravity. It is a very popular idea, popular enough to be spoken of as a Law rather than a theory. The fact that tests to demonstrate the anticipated effects of gravity have not yielded the results anticipated has done little to dampen enthusiasm for such a reasonable, common sense concept. [12] Yes, admittedly the cause of the proverbial apple falling on Newton's head would more evidently be the earth rather than unseen space, and certainly we can rule out the third possibility—the apple itself.

Yet, it seems strange that hundreds of years later, scientists have yet to explain the mechanics of gravity. How does an object extend an influence across millions of miles of empty space instantly?[13] The answer has to do with light and darkness. Light is the fundamental unit of matter; having minimal mass, it also possesses energy. A larger object contains more mass and greater energy. Science has yet to define what energy really is.[20] They are hoping to arrive at an explanation of how all forms of energy—the weak and the strong nuclear forces, electromagnetism and gravity—may be understood as one force. However gravity is the odd force out.[14] This is because gravity was the wrong guess by Newton. Matter actually possesses a repellant (positive) rather than an attractive force (negative). How would this make an apple fall? The apple is acting in response to repelling itself from darkness. The earth is doing the same thing. The earth is not like a rock, held to the sun by a string.[15] It is "hanging upon nothing" ("doesn't matter") (Job 26:7).

It is like a champagne bubble floating in a glass, pushing out in all directions. That literal bubble travels up in response to the overall pressure it encounters in the glass. In the same way, the apple moves down in response to the void in darkness below it (caused by the presence of the earth). All matter is affected by the condition of darkness as a whole, the distortion of which is caused by the presence of all matter. The term for this buoyancy, mistaken for gravity, is "booty" (from the middle German "bute," meaning "exchange"). Note: If you care to celebrate this discovery with a bottle of champagne, allow me to make a suggestion—actually two suggestions:

1. Be careful of a cork in the eye.
2. Rather than try to twist the cork out (because, after all, it is smaller), hold the cork and turn the bottle (because, after all, it is bigger).

I try to decide if something is true on the basis of whether or not it works.

After you finish the bottle, (you don't want to let it go flat) lay it on its side on a table. Put the cork in the bottle. Imagine the bottle to be space (a still sea of darkness) and the cork a star across space. Now push the bottom of the bottle. How long did it take the cork to move? (Even an intoxicated person can perform this experiment.) In the same way, booty (mass pressure) is projected to all parts of space instantly.[16] Heat and booty (exchange) are the same thing (see appendix C). Fact: Energy influences all of darkness at once, with a force inversely proportional to the square of the distance. Ps. 19:6 says of the sun, "And there is nothing concealed from its heat." Heat is the property of all light. Heat is the expansion of light and contraction of darkness. Cold is the opposite. Cold is the expansion of darkness and contraction of light. The universe is a closed system. Heat reduces cold and vice versa. The two strive to exist in equilibrium. The second law of thermodynamics is the expression of this reality. For every action there is an equal and opposite reaction. Simple Physics. Entropy drives the arrangement. Cold and heat will not cease (Gen. 8:22). They will continue to craze and crack things by expansion and contraction.

How then does gravity work? First let me clarify that we're still talking about what can be called gravity. We're just making a distinction as to how it works. Objects still fall. The distinction is that this is due to a pushing force on the part of the object, not a pulling force on the part of a larger object. Also, the distortion of space, Einstein's "bowling ball on a rubber sheet" analogy, is reversed.[17] An object like the sun still distorts space (actually darkness) but not by drawing it in, but by stretching it outward. An object moves in response to all such distortion. In fact, an object, comet, planet, or star moves in response to universal distortion. Darkness is all distorted by matter.

Darkness serves as the gravitational field. It is most stretched in the interior of an object, the earth for instance. Here darkness is most rarified at the earth's core by means of compression. Darkness is displaced at the earth's surface. The heat of the earth stretches darkness outward. This is true of all radiating bodies. Darkness becomes more dense as one elevates. An object let go at arms length finds itself suspended in space. It responds by opposing all darkness at once, just like it had been doing previously. The void in darkness within the earth is the strongest influence on the object. Hence it falls, actually being pushed downward, not pulled. Picture darkness as containing a fine gauze.[18] Stars produce stretch areas in this fine gauze. You can see these in space. What you are actually seeing is the light of the star stretching an area of darkness. Matter gravitates toward the area of lesser darkness.

This is why the moon and other celestial objects orbit. Booty or heat repels them from darkness. Darkness fills space. They are suspended like bubbles in a sea of champagne, not like rocks on strings. Planets are really weightless, made of light. They are pressure driven. It's a beautiful thing: Simple Physics. No gravitons. No gravity waves. No mysterious mechanics, just Simple Physics.

Consider the popular but clumsy illustration of the cannon ball fired around the earth. If fired at sufficient speed and trajectory it would eventually "fall" into an orbit that could maintain itself like the moon. This may work for a while with rockets, but the illustration fails to account for a third factor—the gravitational attraction of the accelerating body itself. What prevents the combined pull of the moon and earth from causing them to "fall" into one another? The phenomenon of tides leads physics to conclude such pulling exists, but is it really pulling? (Why have the mechanics of gravity[12] never been discovered?[13] Could it be because the pulling force we are looking for does not exist?)

Newton; Go Fig. Attractive gravity takes its position alongside other seemingly reasonable but preposterous "scientific" ideas of history: An earth supported on turtles or by Atlas rather than hanging upon nothing; a flat earth rather than spherical; an earth sculpted by vast ice sheets moving "down" from the north rather than by water in a Noachian deluge; millions of unique, self-sustaining life forms generated by evolution rather than a wise, powerful, and loving creator (Job 26:7; Isa. 40:22; Gen. 7:11, 17-20; Gen. 1:24-28, 2:19; Ps. 104:24-25). This was not creationism but, simply, creation.

Lets return to Newton's apple. When its stem broke it was like removing the cork from a bottle of champagne. Like a bubble, the apple was now free to move. It moved in response to the medium surrounding it. The apple drove itself towards the earth rather than being pulled.

The apple, like all matter, was pushing out in a distorted field of darkness. Its movement was driven by its heat, which rises (add some thrusters and you have rocket science). The apple's own mass pushed it away from the denser darkness above it.

So don't be shocked. "Scientific" notions have been turned on their heads before. For example, the wind (Hebrew Ruach, spirit see Gen 1:26 Ftn.) doesn't blow-it sucks or draws (see Jn 6:44). Same effect, different mechanics.

We've discovered something similar with gravity. There is an opposite cause for the observed effect. Objects are not pulled down, they are pushed—by themselves.

The simplest explanation of gravity is that it is an expression of the law of thermodynamics—heat and cold. The predominance of cold (darkness) above an object repels the heat (light) downwards. We see this thermodynamic effect expressed as gravity.

"Facts which at first seem improbable will... stand forth in naked and simple beauty."—Galileo Galilei

Matter is light. This is demonstrated by the fact that all material objects radiate, or give off light. Further, material bodies have the ability to absorb light, becoming more energetic or obtaining more heat.[19] Thus the light of which a material object consists achieves equilibrium in keeping with the laws of thermodynamics.

Matter is something that exists. For anything to exist it must comply with certain parameters. Those parameters are M(T)V[E] (pronounced as in "I want my MTV"). What constitutes M(T)V[E]? [20]

M= **Mass**–the measure of something's ability to distort darkness

(T)= **Time**–the quantity of space that light (matter) occupies, the present

V= **Velocity**–the rate of change in the position of something relative to darkness

[E]= **Energy**–the amount of work required to produce distortion of darkness by something (heat or booty)

All matter exists in darkness. Matter's existence impacts darkness. The nature of space is such that even the existence of a single electron is like the pea under the princess's pile of mattresses. The basic players in the drama are light and darkness. They are opposites. "What sharing does the light have with darkness?" (2 Cor. 6:4). Yet God is "forming light and creating darkness" (Isa. 45:7). They comprise a two-part system. All matter is comprised of light. Outer space consists of darkness and "doesn't matter." The "doesn't matter" is nothing. It has no time (like zero in mathematics), yet imposes structure on outer space. Darkness, on the other hand, is not nothing— but neither is it something. Being the opposite of light (or matter), which exists, darkness is "nonexistent" (Isa. 40:17). What are the parameters of nonexistence?

Negative M= the measure of the distortion of darkness

Negative (T)= the quantity of space darkness (antimatter) occupies, past and future

Negative V= the rate of change in darkness as something moves relative to it.

Negative [E]= the potential of darkness to replace something (bounce)

Picture an hourglass. It marks time by means of an exchange. When it is turned, the sand runs from the top, through the neck, to the bottom. At the same time, air is forced from the bottom to the top, air we can't see and perhaps don't even think about, air that breaks apart to accommodate the sand, air that is dominated by the sand. The air represents darkness. The sand represents light (matter).

The universe works on the same simple principals. It marks time by means of an exchange, an exchange of light and darkness. Light moves. When it does, darkness accommodates it. The movement of the light marks time. The reason the arrangement works is because it is, like the hourglass, a closed system. The universe has an edge (Job 38:19, 20) that contains it, just as an hourglass has glass (a supercooled liquid). Like glass, the edge is uncrazed, frozen darkness, rigid, stiff.

The universe, unlike the hourglass, runs perpetually. This is because the universe is a totally independent, self-contained system. This clock winds itself. The distortion produced in darkness by light in turn drives the light. In the same way, a photon is projected across space without losing any energy. It is the ultimate expression of the interaction of light and darkness.

I could illustrate the hourglass using fine champagne bubbling up instead of common sand falling down. This would demonstrate how the arrangement works without gravity, but the illustration is a little complicated. I don't believe you should have to explain a good illustration too much. Anyway, a bubbling arrangement or a falling one both mark time, but the bubbling one is more evidently pressure driven, like the universe. That's the only point I wanted to get across: the universe does not run by gravity, though it may give that appearance (We're just used to looking at it that way.

Before that, it was winged angels hidden behind the planets). So it seems the universe is not quite as simple as an ordinary hourglass, but it is close (actually it's a little simpler). The universe is not so out of control.

All motion is a change in the position of matter relative to darkness. In its simplest form, it is an expression of the interplay of light and darkness. Matter consists of light and varying amounts of inner space (see appendix C). Darkness is by nature still. Light, even in the form of dense, cold matter, retains some motion. Absolute zero has yet to be and cannot be achieved (Ps. 19:6). How does a photon of light move? How does it embark on a journey across space and not lose velocity or energy? (Job 38:24).[21]

Picture a radiating photon as a hard white ball. The ball is about to enter a room packed with soft black rubber balls. No space exists in the room, only cracks at regular intervals among the black balls. As the white ball enters, it compresses all the black balls. As the white ball pushes forward, the compression is released behind it, pushing the white ball forward. This happens instantly and maintains the velocity with which the white ball entered the room. This is the reason light travels as a wave. It is simply an expression of how light of a given mass responds to a uniform field of darkness. The wave path is in fact a distortion of darkness caused by light, just as orbits are for stars and planets. Light has too much speed (linear velocity) or not enough mass, to close an orbit.

Six Easy Pieces p. 93: "Galileo discovered a very remarkable fact about motion... That is the principle of inertia: If something is moving, with nothing touching it and completely undisturbed, it will go on forever, coasting at a uniform speed in a straight line (Why does it keep on coasting? We do not know, but that is the way it is.)."

Feynman here poses a question which conventional physics is unable to answer. This is because they fail to consider all motion as taking place at a subatomic level, in a field of darkness. For an object to move, every atom within it must move. Those atoms consist of light or heat. They move through what seems like empty space by means of their interaction with darkness. The manner of motion is the same as that of the photon in the room of black balls. There is an exchange, light and darkness, heat and cold. An object or body has a certain amount of freedom, freedom to move where it can. This movement, however, must be within the field of darkness. Darkness facilitates the motion, making it possible by an exchange of negative energy, thermodynamics. This law of exchange must be complied with by everything that moves. For every action there is an equal and opposite reaction. Simple Physics.

A similar situation exists in outer space. This is how a photon "distributes itself " (Job 38:24) through the darkness, yet the darkness maintains its naturally still condition. Light (as well as all matter) exerts a force (called booty) on darkness. For every action, there is an equal and opposite reaction. In the case of light, its velocity (M(T)V[E]) causes darkness to be compressed. The darkness encountered by light instantly rebounds behind the light. This is possible only due to the presence of "doesn't matter," nothing, zero time. "Doesn't matter" is what allows things (existent and nonexistent) to move. It provides that potentiality (Acts 17:28). It is the expression of a law; a tool, like zero. Even nonexistence (darkness) exists in a negative sense (Isa. 41:29). Only "doesn't matter" is truly nothing (yet still a potentiality), a feature of the arrangement of reality. God did not make something out of nothing. Nothing is itself a creation (Rom. 8:39). God made nothing so he would have a place for everything. Simple Physics. Scientists don't know nothing. No, that is not a double negative, and I didn't say scientists know nothing. They know something about some things. They are just yet to acquaint themselves with the nature of nothing ("doesn't matter," time). Nothing changes everything. This is the decade of the "naughts," the decade in which we discovered nothing. A big emphasis is finally going to be put on nothing. It will be seen to be really something. It's like a hole (for a foundation); dig it?

How does Simple Physics affect the laws of motion? They do not change. Galileo was right on. It does however affect the scale of those laws. Galileo identified laws of common motion, motion on a macro scale. But every movement on a macro scale is the result of movement on a micro scale, the subatomic world. The little pieces need to move in order for the big whole to move. This movement is constant. Velocity is a parameter of existence. Matter must move in order to exist. This movement takes place within a field of darkness. Darkness is still, so when matter or light moves, it moves relative to darkness. Darkness exists in tiny details or cubes, solid but soft. Matter is comprised of light. Light of sufficient mass does not radiate as a wave, but orbits around darkness, like a cubic bubble, hollow but hard. Details of darkness, bubbles of light. These are the building blocks of which the universe is made. That's all there is (except for "doesn't matter", the crazes, the potentialities for time). Simple Physics. When light moves, it does not take darkness with it. There is an exchange. After all, it's all darkness and is everywhere that light isn't, so that's where light moves. Light moves where it can. Therein we have a fundamental law of Simple Physics: Light moves where it can. This is true in both the micro and macro worlds. Remember, light is hard. If it runs into itself, there is a collision, like two billiard balls. Darkness is like the felt-covered slate, it allows the billiard balls to move where they can. They can't move through another ball, so they move somewhere else. In their new position, the balls sit on different felt. It's all the same slate and felt. Similarly, darkness is homogeneous; it all works the same way. The darkness which comprises the center of an atom does not move with an atom. The darkness is still and simply facilitates the light around it. It moves radiant light as a wave and moves material light (orbital) as an atom. To be accurate, the atom is moving itself. The heat of the atom provides the positive energy needed for the motion. Darkness only has negative energy, responsive energy.

How does the light distribute itself? By an exchange with darkness. This exchange keeps the light moving, "keeps the ball rolling" so to speak. Heat provides for all motion. For every action there is an equal and opposite reaction. Why is that true? Why is it true even at a micro scale? Because of the fundamental relationship between light and darkness. There is an exchange, a ransom. It's Simple Physics. I'm telling you, you can't make up this kind of stuff. "Galileo discovered a very remarkable fact about motion… that is the principle of inertia. If something is moving with nothing touching it and completely undisturbed, it will go on forever, coasting at a uniform speed in a straight line. (Why does it keep on coasting? We do not know, but that is the way it is.)" (*Six Easy Pieces* p. 93). The previously unknown answer is supplied by Simple Physics. It is due to the exchange between light and darkness. This moves matter at a micro level in the same fashion as a photon is moved thorough space, a piece at a time. For every action, there is an equal and opposite reaction. So why doesn't a photon get pushed backwards when it encounters darkness? There are two reasons. First, darkness is likened to a "vast watery deep" in the Hebrew Scriptures. It fills in behind a photon as the photon passes through it. Secondly, the universe, all of space, is a supersaturated (see ftn Ps 23:5) closed system. The stupid sign at gatherings, "space is limited" begins to make sense. This arrangement allows light to "distribute itself". Light supplies the energy by heat, but it loses no energy to darkness which responds with negative energy. Thank God for dumb darkness.

Science abounds with conservation laws. Foremost among these is the conservation of energy. This law is valid because the universe is a closed system, finite. Remember how Yahowah is able to measure it with the span of his hand? Einstein discussed relativity (see appendix F), yet in order for things to be relative, it must be in relation to something that is absolute (like the size of God's hand). Einstein also had the conviction that "God does not play dice with the universe," implying his laws and standards eliminate chance from reality. Science today, however, seems to feel that if there is a god, he "plays marbles with the universe," sending certain marbles out of the circle by means of black holes and eventually wiping the circle out of the dirt and going home—a poor winner. Simple Physics implies that, rather than the above scenarios, God plays pool with the universe. All the balls are unique—different colors, numbers; yet the same size and weight, hardness. When a rack is broken to begin the game, the balls are not annihilated; they simply assume a different place determined by the force brought to bear on them. They move about a field of felt and slate that doesn't budge. The distribution of the balls is always unique, and due to the skill of the player, they never leave the table. Neither does the player scratch. The white ball, the administrator of the force that drives the other balls, never disappears. If a ball should encounter a hole at the edge of the table, it reemerges in no time to rejoin the rack and continue the games.

What's the game? Certainly not straight pool, eight ball or nine ball, but a combination of all three—screwball. Only God plays it. He makes all fifteen balls in order with the eight (black) ball last. It's hard, but fun. For variety, God racks the balls in a different order each time. He makes every ball off each break. And guess what? He calls the pockets (so you know it isn't luck) (Isa. 65:11, Luke 1:37). God keeps running the table. God keeps racking them up. Every game is different, yet every game is the same. I think it's interesting. If you think it's boring, maybe you're just jealous of God. He's good.

Science is aware of conservation of mass, velocity and energy (M(T)V[E]). What about time? Waste not, want not. God doesn't waste time. Time is space. It is neutral. It does not really change due to an operation. For example $V=(T)$: As velocity increases, time increases. But time is nothing so how can zero be multiplied? A mathematical operation involving time does not really describe what happens. What about infinity? This cannot be reduced by an operation, yet time can be. One can have less time. This is because time is neither zero nor infinity. It is time.

Present mathematical functions do not apply to it. What does apply to it is the fact it is conserved. It is only used as needed. It is always available, but never wasted. Where it runs out (at the edge) other time is available to take its place. Thus light becomes darkness by means of flippancy. How is this darkness replaced? Radiated light is not wasted. Eventually it travels throughout space to the edge. The edge is undifferentiated darkness (Job 38:19, 20): "As for darkness, where, now is its place, that you should take it to its boundary…and that you should understand the roadways to its house?" Job 28:3: "An end to the darkness he has set; and to every limit he is searching out." The crazes end. Light freezes. It is absorbed. Light goes out of existence, adding to darkness. The fabric of darkness is now larger and expands to replace the darkness consumed by stars. This cycle is eternal. It's called flippancy. By means of it an exchange (booty) takes place, a ransom. Floppency is offset by its opposite, flippancy. It all balances out, perfectly, eternally (Rom. 1:20). In this way the supersaturated (Ps. 23:5 ftn) universe of light and darkness never runs out of time. Like a perfect pour, it has just enough space, and will have eternally.

Big things maintain big time. The biggest time is that maintained by all the stars and matter in the universe moving in concert with one another. This represents the universe's absolute clock, driven by the distortion of all space by all matter—the interplay of light and darkness, which cannot touch one another. This clock is self-winding. The past replaces the future as it is moved through by the present. The present drives both the past and future. Distortion is generated as distortion is replaced. For this clock to run requires a closed system of a finite nature. Because of this, and conservation of time, there is always tension on the spring. God wound the clock when he created light and darkness, matter and outer space and the nature of the relationship between them. Ultimately nothing is gained and nothing is lost. For every action there is an equal and opposite reaction. "One thing leads to another." That's Simple Physics. We've looked at $V=(T)$ expressing the conservation of velocity and time. Not to be overlooked are energy and mass.[22] Their conservation is expressed as:

$E=M$ (not $E=MC^2$) (see Isaiah 40:25, 26)

The nature of energy. Energy does not exist apart from matter. Matter has energy by virtue of its existence. It is inherent (there's a big word from my debate days). There is also negative energy. This does not exist apart from antimatter. It is only manifest in response to positive energy. That's what makes it negative. How else could something like energy be negative? I ask you. Nothing bizarre about it. Energy is simply a manifestation of what something is (or isn't in the case of $-E$). This is expressed as $E=M$. Energy equals mass. Mass is energy. Energy is everything that mass is. Isn't that enough? Who came up with $E=MC^2$? Do we have to make energy bigger by some huge and arbitrary factor? Why isn't E big enough on it's own? How are you going to make mass bigger than it already is, and this by the speed of light squared? What's the speed of light got to do with how much energy is in mass? Just assign E a greater value and say E=M. That's all there is. Simple Physics.

That means these parameters are one and the same. Scientists presently acknowledge that matter is a form of energy. Yet they have trouble defining what energy really is.[20] Energy does not exist apart from mass. Light has mass. Light has energy (even cold light has heat). Mass distorts darkness and we call that ability energy. One does not exist apart from the other. In fact, we can say, "I want my MTV," and not worry that we're leaving something out. Drop the E, it's the same as M. The MTV left with the photon. More than mass left because the atom is now occupying less space, some time has left. Since the atom has ability to hold that electron out, thus distorting darkness, energy (or booty) has left! The atom has cooled off or slowed its molecular motion, thus velocity has left, and since mass has left, it distorts less darkness. Oh wait, we already said that, and we all know how we feel about redundancy. So we'll just simply say E=M. The opposite happens when a photon is absorbed by an object. MTV is added to—stronger, bigger, faster. So we'll no longer speak of energy, but rather booty (although it sounds a little cheeky). Booty is heat, the whole energy enchilada—mass energy, kinetic energy, potential energy, nuclear energy, etc., etc., boiled down to, well…a big mass of mass.

Booty (heat) provides the energy that darkness recoils in response to (bounce, negative E).

Stars do not burn out. "Praise him you sun and moon. Praise him all you stars of light. And he keeps them standing forever, to time indefinite. A regulation he has given, and it will not pass away" (Ps. 148:3, 6). Scientists estimate the sun burns 564 million tons of hydrogen per second by thermonuclear reactions. This becomes 560 million tons of helium with a net loss of four million tons per second. All 564 million tons are lost as fuel. How long can that go on? You do the math, but I think it's short of forever. For it to be maintained forever requires a cleaner, more efficient means of burning: a type of fire that is perfectly efficient and clean. A major clue to identifying this fire is at Psalm 148:3, "stars of light." Stars are not simply balls of gas, but orbs of light, wavelengths of energy. Stars contain rarified darkness, mostly raw light which scientists call plasma. This light is so dense or concentrated that it totally distorts the fabric of darkness. Darkness (crazed by time, "doesn't matter") becomes totally occupied by light. A place is no longer found for darkness. Darkness is not pressed out of existence, but rather pressed into existence as light. It's (negative) MTVE or parameters of nonexistence are reversed by floppency. Psalm 139:12: "Even the darkness itself would not prove too dark for you, but night itself would shine just as the day does; the darkness might just as well be the light" (ftn lit. "Like the darkness, like the light;" or, "as the darkness, so the light").

Darkness is the opposite of light; negative light, antilight, antimatter. The presence of a star in the field of darkness distorts darkness. Einstein said massive bodies distorted space like bowling balls on a rubber sheet. Darkness is that rubber sheet, only it is distorted outward like an inflatable rubber ball. Darkness gives structure to space (crazed by "doesn't matter"). The manner of distortion is inward (outside of matter the distortion is outward). In other words, a star does not strictly displace darkness to the outside, rather it also compresses it to the inside and eventually swallows it into itself. Darkness, having been negative, is forced into existence as positive light or energy. This happens as each star sweeps through space in its assigned orbit (Judg. 5:20, Jude 13). Each star is actually consuming darkness as it makes its way through the ocean of space.

A practical application

The power of the sun (solar power) can be captured or replicated by concentrating light. Concentrating light impacts darkness. It is the opposite of obtaining absolute zero. Concentrating light eliminates the (-) MTVE of darkness, forcing it into existence as light. Light prevails over darkness, compressing it by means of booty. Once critical mass is achieved, the engine would continuously run as it moves naturally through darkness. Darkness is antimatter. Light/energy would be produced with only darkness as fuel. We know this can be achieved because the stars are antimatter engines burning eternally (Ps. 148:3, 6, Rom. 1:20). We can build tiny stars (Gen. 11:6, "Nothing…unattainable"). This would be by simply shining or concentrating a beam into a closed, mirrored orb. You would find you're suddenly getting more light out than you are putting in. That's the simple description of an AME (Anti-Matter Engine) pronounced "AIM" (as in "Ready, Aim, Fire"). An engineer could improve the design. Run a contest. But try it yourselves (I can't build one in my basement). You'd get a lot more bang for your buck than you do with "particle accelerators." Antimatter is not the cold dark enemy. It's really friendly, warm. It just needs a big hug. The condensing of the light would actually cool it, so the project is not as dangerous as it sounds (in the same way as the sun's surface being far cooler than the corona). *Geo* (Sun) July 2004 p. 7: "Why is the halo-like corona hundreds, even thousands of times hotter than the surface? That's one of the questions that keep scientists looking straight at the sun."

Puzzle solving for pre-kindergartners.

This is the one Einstein worked on for his last 30 years. He called it the search for a unified field, but we can call it odd pegs in a round hole. You start with four pegs and one round hole, to make it interesting (a real brain buster). The pegs are oval, triangle, square and round. The hole is round. Examine the pegs one at a time with your chubby little hands. They are all interesting, but only one is nice and round. The other three can be set aside. Now take the last remaining peg, the round one, and slip it smoothly into the round hole. It's the only one that fits. Congratulations, Junior, you've solved the puzzle of the varied pegs in the round hole. Simple Physics. Can it really be that easy? You just saw that it was. Unfortunately for Einstein, he just didn't get it, but it's the only way to solve the puzzle (that is without getting out the power tools or a really big mallet—equipment they don't allow in nursery school).

Do you think you could have done it without me walking you through it? Of course you say. That's an insult! But Albert Einstein worked on it for 30 years. That's the nature of Simple Physics. It's like darkness. It's right in front of us. But no one sees it. Simple Physics is, well, simple. There is a unified field, a single force that drives the universe. It's called heat. Warm up to the idea.

Heat and cold are opposites. Light is heat, darkness is cold. Darkness is as cold as it gets. Light gets as hot as it can. Wait, did I say that correctly? Darkness is cold, yes. Darkness is cold, the same thing. You can't have cold without darkness. Where there is darkness heat is missing (radiant light of all wavelengths) allowing for darkness or cold to be present. Cold equals darkness. Absolute zero has a temperature assigned to it. Darkness is cold and absolute zero defines how cold that is. Light is heat. Is it therefore the opposite temperature that absolute zero is? How can you have an opposite temperature when temperatures are measured on the same scale? What we can say is that cold is limited. It's opposite, heat, is not. The speed of light is not limited. Unlike cold, which is still and can get no stiller, heat has no maximum value. It's an expression. The value C is a constant at which light is radiated. It is not the maximum speed of light. Why not? Because light is the opposite of darkness and darkness has a limit.

The equivalency principle.[23] We've already learned that E=M. Is this equivalency true of the remaining parameters of existence? Yes and no. It is true of velocity. Velocity has in common with E and M that it too is an expression of force. Velocity equals energy. Velocity equals mass.[24] MVE is force that increases or decreases together. MVE are expressions of the same thing, equivalent. Time on the other hand, is a horse of a different feather. There is nothing like time. Nothing equals time because time is nothing and everything else is something. Sound like double talk? That's why the equivalency principle is a double principle. The second part of it is expressed as MVE/T or M/T, V/T, E/T. Everything changes over time. Time itself is unaffected; a true constant. It only changes in relation to light and darkness within it, and then the change is only in a mathematical sense. The more nothing (time) there is, the less there will be of the other thing. Like when your pen starts to run out of ink, the more skips, the less ink. (Funny how that works.) It's an expression of the equivalency principle. MVE are equivalent. If one increases, they all increase and time increases. But wait! What are we talking about here? Time is nothing. If a clock is moving slow or fast, the sum is still zero. So don't let a clock fool you, it's just a tool, Einstein. The luminaries were to "serve as signs," (Gen 1:14) but they were not time itself.

M(T)VE are all equal in one sense. They are all parameters of existence. If you could eliminate one of them (as in the efforts to achieve absolute zero) you would eliminate all of them. The thing being frozen would cease to exist. Light would become darkness (nonexistence). This is impossible for the same reason perpetual motion is impossible. It is impossible to fabricate a totally independent system (see Ps 19:6). The only truly self-contained system is the universe itself. In it, absolute zero is obtained at the edge by means of flippancy. An exchange occurs by means of floppency, energy being brought into existence by stars. This too is a manifestation of conservation of energy. Flippancy and floppency are equal. Nothing is wasted. Nothing is lost. How does this impact the search for a "unified field?" Einstein spent 30 fruitless years in this pursuit because someone slipped him the wrong pieces to the puzzle. Science recognizes four fundamental forces. Are these somehow expressions of a single force? Simple Physics states that reality is the expression of force (Isa 40:26c) over time. How are the four forces reduced to one? Let's consider them one at a time.

Gravity

Einstein was left with Newton's legacy, an idea that was, unfortunately, incorrect. Scientists have long been baffled by gravity which has been termed "the odd force out" because of its imagined nature, to pull things toward its source.[25] No mechanics for gravity have ever been found, although several experiments have been conducted which contradict its anticipated effects. Chapter two of this book proposed a stark alternative to gravity: that matter exists in a supersaturated field of darkness and is buoyed by heat. Gravity is an oval peg for a round hole. It will never work, even if the puzzle solver is Albert Einstein.

Strong nuclear force

Here is another funny force. It came into vogue when a simple observation was made about the atomic model. The protons at the nucleus of an atom are positively charged. Like repels like. That is a very strong force to counteract. The solution: Invent an even stronger force to glue the protons together. Invent a cute name for the carriers of the force. Call them gluons. Problem solved. Only with Simple Physics there is no problem. The concept with Simple Physics is that light orbits darkness. Darkness constitutes the interior of the atom. Darkness also makes up a field surrounding the atom. Light moves within this field. The details that make up the darkness are interchangeable. Hey, it's all darkness. Darkness is negative and still. No force is necessary in order to hold it together. (By the way, in the atomic model electrons are labeled negative and protons positive. This designation is arbitrary. In Simple Physics light is always positive, because it has the outward pressure of heat. Darkness is negative because its energy is reactive, only manifesting itself in response to heat.) So the strong nuclear force was invented to solve a problem that doesn't exist. Yet its existence produced a problem for Einstein, this time a triangular peg for a round hole.

Weak nuclear force

The weak nuclear force is a square peg. What are we talking about weak forces for anyway? It's an oxymoron. Again, this force was invented to solve a problem with the atomic model. Admittedly, I don't know all I should about the development of the theory, but I imagine it went something like this: You've got negatively charged electrons circling positively charged nuclei and you notice that, despite being of opposite charges, they are not sticking to one another. Why not? Oh, there must be a force we have just discovered that holds the electrons out from the nucleus. The force is weak because it is broken when atoms exchange electrons in chemical reactions, so we'll call it the weak nuclear force. Is that somewhat close? We've already defined darkness and light as negative and positive. Does this mean they oppose one another? No. It means they work together like compliments. Darkness operates off the energy of light. Light uses darkness to "distribute itself" (Job 38:24). Light is suspended between darkness and darkness by means of heat. Again, no imaginary weak nuclear force is necessary.

Electromagnetic force

Now we're onto something. This force actually works. We now have a round peg for a round hole. Electromagnetism embodies all forms of radiant energy, aka heat (heat is electromagnetic). Heat is the only force there is. Light is heat. Electromagnetic radiation: lightening in a bottle. Heat drives everything. For every action by heat there is an equal and opposite response by cold darkness. Together they drive things, eternally. Simple heat, too simple to even be listed among the fundamental forces, is the solution to Einstein's puzzle. The Bible in speaking of the sun at Psalm 19:6 provides a key clue, "and there is nothing concealed from it's heat." The force, the energy, the heat of the sun literally reaches all things. It shares the present with all other matter, all light. That force which stretches the superfine gauze amid darkness is heat. Heat is the unified field.

Time originated before the universe (compare Jn 1:1 and Gen 1:1). God created time so he would have a place to put things. God existed before time. He uses it as a tool. We have "time indefinite" in our hearts (Eccl 3:11). We perceive time as existing, the duration or span of our existence, the period for which we occupy space. In the previous discussion of light, it was explained that in order for something to exist, it must possess time. Time was defined as the quantity of space something occupies.

"As apples of gold in silver carvings is a word spoken at the right time for it" (Prov 25:11). Each apple is in its assigned setting or place. These settings (carvings) are the same only different, equivalent to time in the scripture. Many apples are likened to a single word since that word has many right times or settings, places, any of which could be the proper time. Also time is not singular. No single moment or point of time exists. It changes from future to present to past instantly, in no time. Mr. Heisenberg, how long was the present present? Not very long. Then we're in the next moment of the present. All these concurrent moments comprise present time, a continuum.

The point we want to notice, at this point, is that time is a place. After describing a place (carvings) the scripture does not liken it to "the right place for it." A place is time. A place is space. Therefore time is space. The Bible is not redundant. It does not say, "there is a time and place for everything." It says simply that there is a time for everything (Eccl 3:1a).

Picture space (Rom 8:39). Space is nothing. Yet it is something, a reality (compare Eccl 9:11b). Everything occupies a certain amount of space. If it is so small that it occupies no space, you will never detect it because it does not exist.

Things that do exist possess time, though most matter is unaware of it. As humans we know we occupy space (Eccl 3:11), more specifically inner space we call the present. The present is real. It is the space we exist in (compare Eph 3:18). What of past and future? They do not truly exist. They comprise negative T, or nonexistent time. This is the quantity of space unoccupied by matter and hence occupied by darkness. The past is space that was occupied by matter, the future space that will be occupied. Past and future are determined relative to the present. It's where something has been or will be. We can't touch either one; as far as we're concerned past and future are in reality the same thing, nonexistent.

Rather than think of time as space the size of a breadbox for a breadbox, remember that matter influences or occupies the 'entire universe' (Ps 19:6). This influence is instantaneous, like moving the champagne bottle, and changes instantaneously as an object moves. All matter occupies the present together. As an object moves it remains constantly in the present. It never encounters its past or future because they do not exist. Additionally, the past and future make up outer space, something inner space (the present) never touches due to booty. An object occupies what we call inner space. Beyond its time is outer space. Outer space is space unoccupied by matter. Matter possesses time as one of its parameters of existence. "Doesn't matter" is the potentiality for time to manifest itself. Time is space, the present (inner space). Time is also outer space, space occupied by darkness. This is past and future or nonexistent time. All space is occupied by either darkness or light. It is "saturation itself" (see Ps 23:5 ftn), a closed system. "Doesn't matter" is likewise nothing, a mere potentiality, crazes that are closed until light enters by means of booty. Until then "doesn't matter" is snapped shut by darkness. "For everything there is an appointed time" (Eccl 3:1). Darkness is also a thing (Ex 10:21, Isa 41:29), antimatter (the opposite of light). Matter, by it's existence, utilizes time (positive), by affecting an exchange with time (negative).

This understanding of time is demonstrated by clocks. Clocks are simply set to run at a certain speed. Where their size changes their speed changes.[26] They expand or contract. This is what happens to Einstein's clocks. A clock in a rocket gains velocity, energy and mass and hence time. The clock has actually gotten bigger.[27] It has been demonstrated that a clock elevated on the earth runs faster. This is because the clock is now smaller. It exists in an area of lesser space or positive T. This is due to the distortion of space by the earth: the farther from the earth, the less the distortion and hence less positive time. Smaller clocks run faster. Big clocks keep big time. Their hands make bigger sweeps. Time has only changed relative to the clock. A faster traveling bigger clock is occupying more of it, hence runs slower.[28]

The relationship between size and time can be demonstrated with an hourglass. A bigger hourglass marks slower time. Start with an hourglass filled with tiny ball bearings. Establish that the ball bearings take one hour to fall. Now scale everything up by half; bigger balls, bigger glass, bigger opening. It would take more than an hour for the same number of balls to fall. The glass would run slower. But let's not take over an hour to do the experiment. Let's make a second glass with one ball and another (I'd say a second, but you might get confused) glass, half larger with a larger ball. Turn them at the same time. This turning will require more force (by half) for the second glass or it would be even slower; as it is the second, larger ball, will fall slower (not because it is heavier, as Galileo demonstrated) because it must fall farther. Hence a bigger hourglass runs longer, slower. But wait, in our experiment the big hourglass will run slower. This is because everything was kept proportional. That, however, is not an accurate reflection of the distortion of space. Booty is directional; heat rises. Space is distorted vertically. Things influenced by the field of space become higher more than wider. If this condition is reflected in our second glass, the ball has even farther to fall and it will run even longer. A smaller, shorter glass will run faster. Their speed depends on the condition of the space they occupy. This isn't rocket science, Einstein. It's Simple Physics.

And let me clear something else up: I have a great deal of respect for Albert Einstein (see appendix F), but the man was not a god. Well, actually yes, he was and is a god. But like the others gods men make, he had his foibles. When it came to time, he was a little confused. But at least he had a sense of humor about it. "The king is dead, long live the king!" (compare 2 Chronicles 23:11).

Throughout this discussion, reference has been made to (+) positive and (-) negative time. It should be pointed out that these designations are only mathematical tools. The nature of time remains the same regardless of where it exists. (+)Time and (-) time are what we call common time. Common time can have an operation (+,-,x,/) performed upon it. Absolute time, universal time, defies mathematics. It's different. It is neither positive nor negative. It's neutral, unaffected by what it contains. Time is time, space, nothing. Nothing from nothing leaves nothing. You've still got some of what you already had, nothing. Time doesn't change.

A clock marks common time, the space it possesses. Each clock is unique. You can't build identical clocks, occupying the same amount of space. Every clock is different. They all mark different time. Each is simply a tool.

Time stops for no one, or more accurately, no one stops for time. Time doesn't move, we do, light does. Darkness is by nature still, but constantly compressing and bouncing (like the soft black balls). We move relative to time, but perceive this motion as the passage of time. It is, in fact, the passage of us.

Something will be better or worse over time. We can't evaluate until it happens. What we do know is that it will change, be different. You can't apply a formula to it. Forty-year-old scotch is better but 400-year-old may not be and 4000-year-old is anybody's guess. Time will tell. Time changes things in different ways (Eccl 9:11, 12). It is neither positive nor negative. It's just different. Time is not zero, it is something, and time is not infinite, it is a feature of a closed system. Neither zero (0), nor infinity (∞), it is a sort of clear eight ball or a fly ball. Time is strange. It's screwball ($\emptyset$), universal time.

Time, unlike the other parameters of existence, is not a constant. It's a super constant. It changes constantly. Time doesn't submit to mathematics. You can't assign a value to $\emptyset$. +T and –T are used in dealing with common time, time associated with something, not absolute time, free time (which there is no such thing as—that's a little joke, by the way). Time is nothing. The thing about nothing is that whether you have a little or a lot, it's still nothing. The difference is what it does, what it changes.

In screwball, the 🎱 is not really part of the rack, it doesn't have a number. It rolls independently. It's always moving and is still moving at each break. The balls must each hit the screwball before they go in, in order. The balls kiss it. They all must be made in combination. It's not simple, yet all shots are the same. Screwball is different. Time is different. The screwball is oblong, long in the direction of infinity, short towards zero. It rolls funny. Time changes everything. It makes for a more interesting game. God plays with time. It's a gentleman's game. God doesn't kneel in the dirt to play (like the marbles science has him playing, violently, selfishly). Screwball employs a lot of force without violence. It's cool. That may seem absurdly difficult (you're right, it ain't easy), but give God a little credit. He's made some tricky shots so far (see Job 38:1-7). God can handle it. He likes his games to be interesting.

No, God doesn't play dice with the universe. In reality, neither does he play screwball. His game involves not balls but every element in existence. Simple Physics are the rules of the game (Jer 32:27). Those rules teach us that as velocity increases, mass increases.[24] Correspondingly, energy increases. At the same time common time increases, MTVE exists together. MVE is force within the setting of time. MVE borrows time as it acts. It "takes time." Common time becomes part of force until it runs out at the edge. F/ 🎱 is as far as one can reduce the Equation for Reality. It reads "force over (universal) time", Simple Physics. All of physics can be expressed as force over time (screwball). Screwball: God playing with time. It's all a game of timing. None of the balls ever stop moving. They simply change how they interact.

Instead of looking for twelve dimensions scientists should be recognizing one. Keep it simple. The Bible enumerates four dimensions; breadth, length, height and depth (Eph 3:18). These are four expressions of the same thing, the super dimension. Time. The dimensions are simply tools by which all living things orient themselves. This information can be useful for survival, which living things generally like to do (even lemmings).

Let me get back to the point. Dimensions are not absolute. They depend on your orientation. If one man is on the north pole and another man is at the same time on the south pole height or "up" will not be the same for both men. In fact "up" is not strictly the same for any two men. The dimensions vary according to the space one occupies. They're just tools. They are features of space or time. Time is what God created in order to have a place to put things. Everything occupies time (Eccl 3:1). Think of it as space. Think of it as nothing. God didn't create things out of nothing. He created things into nothing, so he would have a place to put them. Sound too simple? Then tell me again the one about the twelve dimensions.

What is time? The super dimension, space itself. Time is nothing. "Doesn't matter" consists of tiny crazes. How tiny? So tiny that in reality they don't exist. The crazes of "doesn't matter" are always partially open (providing time for light) and partially closed (providing time for darkness). So the crazes exist only as potentialities for time. The crazes exist only in the mind of God. Are we saying God is crazed? No offense intended (Eccl 7:8, 9). God is crazy...but it's a good crazy.

Perhaps we should look at the "mind of Christ" (1 Cor 2:16). He thought like God does. When his relatives heard about what he said and did, "They went out to lay hold of him, for they were saying 'He has gone out of his mind'. Also the scribes,...were saying, 'He has Beelzebub, and he expels the demons by means of the ruler of the demons'" (Mark 3:21, 22). Were these critics correct that Yeshua was crazed? Was it rather not the other way around?

At 1 Samuel 19:20, 23, 24 Saul and his men "began behaving like prophets." Why? "The spirit of God came to be upon them. Saul lay naked all day and night." Crazy? Let's not get into name-calling (compare 2 Kings 9:11). Remember God doesn't play straight pool. God is different. He doesn't think like you and I. He thinks differently. He has a truly beautiful mind.

Mark 12:28-34. Here in response to a scribe's question, Yeshua gives a scriptural answer, but goes beyond what the law said. He adds the requirement of loving Yahowah with one's "whole mind." At Luke 10:25-28 a man gives a similar answer to Yeshua's question, "What is written in the Law? How do you read?" The respondent had not read about the mind in the Hebrew Scriptures. He figured it out on his own, or from Bible teachers. He was told by Yeshua, "You answered correctly; keep on doing this and you will get life." Doing what? Loving God and neighbor and also using our whole mind to draw Bible-based conclusions about God and his mind. God did not have all this information written in a book (John 21:25). What he did have written is complete (2 Tim. 3:16, 17), but it forms only a "pattern of healthful words" (2 Tim. 1:13).

If you ask one of Jehovah's Witnesses where the Bible talks about "new scrolls," he'll open his Bible to Rev. 20:12. Yes, here is the promise of fresh, new information to assist us in the education of resurrected mankind. But the verse does not say "new scrolls," at least mine doesn't. It simply says "scrolls" with a footnote, Lit "little books." Gr., "biblia." It sounds like we're opening up something we already have, the Bible. God's word is deep. Hopefully this little book has heightened your appreciation for it. Don't look past it (John 17:17). Worship the one who has given it as his communication to mankind.

Puzzle Solving (1 Kings 10:1).[29] How do you solve a puzzle? First, open the box (duh?). Embark on the project. Look inside. How do the pieces look? Take a few moments to count them. This is especially important if someone has had the puzzle before you. They may have lost some pieces or their dog chewed them up, and there is nothing more disappointing or frustrating than attempting a puzzle with missing pieces. Counting is not too hard a job. There should be twelve. Pay attention now. You may have noticed there's a limited amount of nothing in the box, too. Don't forget it. You'll need some nothing to put the puzzle together. Of course it can be any nothing, not just the nothing that comes with the puzzle. It's all the same, but how you use it makes a difference. Then take the pieces out of the box (think outside the box). This gives one room to operate (we say "one" because this is an individual, solitary exercise, just you). Notice there are a finite number of pieces, so it can be solved. Find a flat, hard surface (not a feather bed) on which to assemble the pieces (this surface represents one's "power of reason," (Rom. 12:1)). Begin by looking for four double straight pieces, the corners (the corners are M[T] VE, the parameters of all things, both (+) existent and (-) nonexistent). The corners fit the straight pieces together, forming them into a frame. A piece is recognized for straightness based on God's Word, the Bible (God's straightedge, 2 Tim. 3:16, 17). (Hey, if you don't like that maybe you should find another puzzle to work on, because this one has a lot of straight edges.) This ain't no 1500 piece jigsaw made for only intellectual adults. It's simple. The puzzle you pulled out of the box is for young children (Matt. 18:3). It's not even a picture puzzle, or did you notice? A picture is too static, too restrictive. This puzzle has a "pattern" (Heb. 8:5) made out of primary colors (red, green, blue). The colors move to produce all the colors (the puzzle spins, appearing white, circular). Kids like it, they think it's cool.

The puzzle we are looking at is the universe. Still a little confused? Try the puzzle the hard way, like blind people do. Turn all the pieces upside down (you may have noticed they're only colored, shiny, on the top side). Now try to get a better feel for it. Feel the edges, slide the pieces around the hard flat surface. That's like seeing darkness as the flipside to the puzzle. Darkness is the opposite of light—flat black. Science pretends darkness isn't there. Science is blinded by the light (Lk 6:39, 40). They need a good pair of shades. Then they could be cool like us kids who appreciate the universe for what it really is (compare Jn 9:39-41), simply awesome. With a puzzle, the parts make up the whole. The universe has only two fundamental constituents, force, expressed as MVE, and time (pieces of nothing). Don't forget the puzzle has two sides, light and darkness. Time provides space for each. It was in the box too, you just couldn't see or feel it. Darkness is negative force, (-)MVE. I hope you can follow this, because I'm making it as simple as I can, kid.

How simple is this puzzle? Why could a blind kid do it backwards? First of all, it has a finite number of pieces, twelve.[30] All the pieces are the same (equivalency principle) only different. Not only the corners, but all the pieces are square, having four straight edges.[31] The puzzle assembles in the shape of a square. In order for that to happen with twelve pieces, four pieces must be missing from the middle (no, this is not the missing dark matter. It is time, nothing, the pieces we can't see. They are not missing, but fit anywhere they are needed). This means every piece is part of the framework and the puzzle is doubly square (Note: Foursquare, 12 pieces (compare Ezek. 48:15, 16, 31-34). The city, Yahowah "himself is there," is described as being both foursquare and having 12 gates. The gates obviously opened to the inner courtyard making the structure doubly square).

God likes squares. That's why he built the universe out of them. But so he wouldn't bore us, he made everything look round. God is nice that way. He wants us to be happy too. God conceived the puzzle as a square for us to figure initially, simply. But he's given us the power to arrange the pattern any way we want. Kid's puzzles are for fun, not to be brain busters. Who wants a busted brain, anyway? (Rom. 11:33-36; Prov. 25:2, 3; Eph, 3:18, 19).

I'd like to acknowledge the translation committee of the *New World Translation of the Holy Scriptures With References* whose fine Bible translation (quoted throughout this book) helped me to see accurately what I did know, from the Bible. I should also acknowledge the help I received by referring to two volumes by Richard P. Feynmann, "*Six Easy Pieces*" and "*Six Not So Easy Pieces*". Especially appreciated was his humble acknowledgement of what physicists do not know.[32] This was instrumental in formulating "*Simple Physics*". Also useful was Steven Weinburg's "*Dreams of a Final Theory*". This is that theory (actually the "hole" truth, Acts 2:17)[33], although, according to Weinburg, it's probably more like a nightmare. But ultimately all credit goes to Yahowah God for providing the ability to reason, as well as the Book of Creation and the Bible to reason upon. In this way, it can be seen what we may know by his permission (1 Sam 17:40; compare Matt 11:25, Prov 28:1).

Proverbs 14:6 "The ridiculer has sought to find wisdom, and there is none, but to the understanding one knowledge is an easy thing."

Acts 26:8 "Why is it judged unbelievable among you men that God raises up the dead?" (see also Titus 1:1-3). Additional reading, 1 Kings 18: 17-40, James 5:17.

As for me, I'm going to take the advice given by a woman to a woman at Ruth 3:18, "Sit still, my daughter, until you know how the matter will turn out, for the man will have no rest unless he has brought the matter to an end today" (compare Heb 4:7-10). Dear reader, "You da man!" Are you just a reader, or will you do something? Praise Yah, you people! (Psalm 150).

Thank you,

James M. Jacobs
(Heb 11:1,3)
jamesjacobs2080@yahoo.com

Conclusion

This is the way booty works. It's an exchange. Booty is pushing against a field of darkness. Planets float in darkness like bubbles in champagne. They are suspended by mass pressure, booty, which is simply heat. Heat or light energy (remember matter consists of light) opposes darkness or antimatter. The opposite nature of light and darkness is what drives the universe. Everything is conserved. It works because it is a super-saturated closed system. It also works because darkness is crazed (and structured) by "doesn't matter," the potential for time. That's about as simply as I can put it…Thank you. (Don't look now, but I'm going to keep going.)

At the onset, we promised that our study of physics would teach us something about God. Why? Because "his invisible qualities are clearly seen from the world's creation onward…even His eternal power and Godship, so that they are inexcusable" (Rom. 1:20). We leave the reader to draw his own conclusions. Whatever those conclusions may be, I would like to assert this: Any consideration of the Book of Creation is only academic unless it brings us to a more intimate knowledge of the Creator. The Bible, drawn on throughout this little book, is even more helpful in that endeavor. It is likened to a "light" (Ps. 119:105) and as Solomon said "there is more advantage for light than for darkness" (Eccl 2:13).

The Psalmist added, "…the wicked one according to his superciliousness (Lit, "according to the height of his nose") makes no search; all his ideas are there is no God" (Ps. 10:4). This little book was written by someone who tries to see beyond the nose on his face—even in the dark. My idea is "there is a God," and I hope you will one day join me in that conviction, if you are yet to do so. If you presently are of that conviction, it is my earnest prayer that this little book will help you to know him more accurately (compare Rom 10:1-3).

Afterward

The ark of the testimony (Exodus 39:35) represents heavenly things, more specifically God's name (see 2 Sam 6:2). It belonged in the Most Holy. Man's only direct connection to the ark was a set of poles used to carry it. These poles could be seen from the Holy. "But the poles were long, so that the tips of the poles were visible at the Holy in front of the innermost room, but they were not visible outside, and they continue there down to this day" (2 Chron 5:9, 1 Kings 8:8).

These pole tips represent the physical universe, the "heavens." While not heaven itself, they give us insight into what heaven is like (Job 26:14). The universe is a two-part system, light and darkness. Light and darkness are separated by space or time, as the poles were. The poles stuck out into the Holy. Was this intrusion a hazard? Did a person run the risk of bumping his head into one (or, heaven forbid, both)? Only if he were crawling around the floor like an animal and that with his proud head up. A simple observer could appreciate that the poles were "long" (notice not, "too long"). Was the poles' protruding into the Holy a design flaw? We'll pretend we never asked that question. The poles were there, in the open, obvious, in order to teach us something, but what? What are we looking at? Two poles: bipolar. Out-of-place: disorder. Bipolar disorder, manic(light)/depression(darkness). This condition gives insight into heavenly things, but is not to be compared with the insight of those entering the Most Holy (compare 1 Cor. 14:37). Any insight I have received is like seeing shafts of light from within the temple (2 Chron 22:11). These shafts make evident where the cracks are, but to repair them requires the oversight of older men (compare 2 Chron. 24:1, 2, 6a). The anointed remnants are those men (Matt. 24:45-47), the Yahoiada class (2 Chron. 23:1, 8-11).

Appendices

Appendix A

Abyss

"According to Parkhurst's Greek and English Lexicon to the New Testament (London, 1845, p. 2), the Greek a'byssos means "very or exceedingly deep." According to Liddell and Scott's Greek-English Lexicon (Oxford, 1968, p. 4) it means "unfathomable, boundless." The Greek Septuagint uses it regularly to translate the Hebrew "te hohm" (watery deep), as Genesis 1:2; 7:11.

A'byssos occurs nine times in the Christian Greek Scriptures, seven of them being in the book of Revelation. It is from "the abyss" that the symbolic locusts come forth under the headship of their king, Abaddon or Apollyon, "the angel of the abyss" (Rev. 9:11). "The wild beast" that makes them is also spoken of as coming "out of the abyss" (Rev. 11:3, 7). Revelation 20:1-3 describes the future casting of Satan into the abyss for a thousand years; something that a legion of demons urged Jesus not to do to them on a certain occasion. – Luke 8:31.

Scriptural Significance

It is noteworthy that the Greek Septuagint does not use a'byssos to translate the Hebrew she'ohl, and in view of the fact that spirit creatures are cast into it, it cannot properly be limited in meaning to Sheol or Hades, inasmuch as these two words clearly refer to the common earthly grave of mankind (Job 17:13-16; see Hades; Sheol). It does not refer to "the lake of fire," since it is after Satan's release from the abyss that he is thereupon hurled into the lake of fire (Rev. 20:1-3, 7-10). Paul's statement at Romans 10:7, in which he speaks of Christ as being in the abyss, also precludes such possibility and shows as well that the abyss is not the same as Tartarus. – See Tartarus

Romans 10:6, 7 aids in clearing up the meaning of "the abyss" in stating: "But the righteousness resulting from faith speaks in this manner: 'Do not say in your heart, "Who will descend into the abyss?" that is, to bring Christ up from the dead'" (compare Deut. 30:11-13). It is evident that "the abyss" here refers to the place in which Christ Jesus spent part of three days and from which place his Father resurrected him (compare Ps. 71:19, 20; Mt 12:40). Revelation 20:7 refers to the abyss as a "prison," and the confinement of absolute restraint resulting from death in the case of Jesus certainly harmonizes with this (Compare Acts 2:24; 2 Sam. 22:5, 7; Job 38:16, 17; Ps. 9:13; 107:18; 116:3; Jude 13).

Concerning the root meaning "unfathomable" as characteristic of "the abyss," it is of interest to note the statement in Hastings' *Encyclopaedia of Religion and Ethics* (1913, Vol 1, p. 54), which, in commenting on Romans 10:6, 7 says: "The impression conveyed by St. Paul's language is of the vastness of that realm, as one that we should vainly attempt to explore" (Insight on the Scriptures Vol. 1 p. 35).

Both 2 Pet. 2:17 and Jude 13 speak of the "blackness of darkness" as the place of the incorrigibly wicked. Satan leaves the abyss only to return to the "lake of fire" (Rev. 20:14, 15). The lake of fire designates the duration of one's stay in the abyss or darkness. That is why Christ was there only temporarily. A stay in the abyss as the lake of fire is eternal, but it is all the same place—darkness. This is all to show that the abyss is the realm of nonexistence, antimatter, darkness. The abyss and darkness are synonymous.

Appendix B

Big Bang

In a well-filled cup, the liquid is held by surface tension. Another drop could not be added. It is "saturation itself" (Ps. 23:5 ftn). A well-filled cup had to have been poured by someone, a skilled and generous bartender. Light was poured into darkness by the great Bartender, Yahowah God. This was not the Big Bang. This was the "Big Turn On" (as in "Turn on the lights, please."), the "Big Pour."

This resulted in an orderly arrangement. It was a smooth pour, saturation itself (Heb. 3:4; 1 Cor. 14:33a). Nothing spilled on the bar. The pour was perfect. It just makes it so that we have to bow our heads to drink the cup because we can't raise it without spilling (because we're not perfect). The stars are orderly, indicating purposeful design (Judg. 5:20). They are doing an ancient circle dance of victory and celebration (you were expecting maybe a jig, for God's sake?). The Hebrew verb "chul," which basically means "whirl, turn," is also rendered "dance" (Insight on the Scriptures Vol. 1 p. 575). What you get is simple, but elegant. Simple Physics (Job 38:33).

"My cup runneth over" (Ps. 23:5 King James Version). "My cup is well-filled" (NWT ftn Lit., "is saturation itself"). When the universe was created, it was not designed to have huge, empty voids, but was "well-filled." It was filled with darkness, then with light. The darkness received the light, like a bucket of air receiving paint. Light and darkness were boxed together in a closed container. The pigments were distributed around in relation to one another, as we see the stars and galaxies, clusters, superclusters and megacluster (singular). Or if you prefer a less working-class illustration, imagine a pure white cream being added to pitch black coffee. (We'll call them black and white for the purpose of illustration, so lighten up, work with me.) Can you picture the universe like that? Stimulating but at the same time mellow. And don't forget, really good coffee always has bubbles. The cup is well-filled. It was poured by God, either light or darkness exist everywhere. Light produces distortions in darkness, which assures the spaced distribution of heavenly bodies. Light's heat crazed the darkness, producing space for itself, or present time (Gen. 1:1).

The creation of the earth mirrored the creation of the heavens, which had come before it (Gen. 1:2, 3). Darkness, at first, occupied all space (time) prior to the introduction of light. The heat of light (expansion) crazed darkness like the inside of a glazed coffee mug (see cover illustration) into tiny cubes. The crazes ("doesn't matter") were the potentiality for (+) time, occupied by light—the present. Hello? Is anybody (in) out there? Is something going on around here? This was no Big Bang.[34] This was the "Big Turn On," the "Big Pour."

Appendix C

Quantum Mechanics

The superfine field of darkness (darkness and "doesn't matter") does not end at matter (Isa. 40:22). Rather, when light (which matter consists of) has enough mass, its wavelength is short enough to be an orbit. What appear to be photons vary in energy. Energy equals mass (E=M). The mass determines how a photon interacts with the field of darkness. Light travels as a wave. A wave is simply an orbit with a linear component. A radio wave is generated by a wave of very low mass and hence, energy. A gamma ray has enough mass to generate a very short wavelength. Electrons have sufficient mass to generate an orbit. Atoms are mostly empty space. If we look (actually we can't look, which is what makes this theoretical physics) more closely at that space we see it is not empty but completely saturated. Even what is termed inner space is a negatively structured field that distorts but does not move. When matter moves it moves with relation to this field. Matter consists of numerous wave packages of like wavelength or orbits, resonances. [35]

Darkness provides the field that matter (light) is knit around. Light orbits darkness. As light moves, it orbits around different segments of darkness, each being uniform. This shifting does not alter the atom, it simply shapes it. Booty drives the orbit of the atom as it compresses darkness. The orbit is also influenced by the darkness existing outside of it. The sea of darkness is so consistent that atoms remain stable despite their movement relative to it.

A particle is defined by its velocity and time (place) (uncertainty principle).[36] The term particle is a misnomer.[37] Every manifestation of energy is unique. Energy expresses itself in several ways; mass energy (commonly mistaken for gravity, by which matter distorts the whole universe and always has) and energy of motion by which matter moves (velocity). It's all the same energy expressing where it is concentrated. This is known as heat. A particle is a convenient way to picture it, but it is no more a solid object than a planet is. I don't mean to produce an entire dissertation on Quantum Mechanics here. To be honest, the whole study is a little confusing to me. Some of my ideas may be wrong, but this one is right. Darkness is the opposite of light and atoms consist of light and darkness…period.[38]

Appendix D

Bubbles

Everything is bubbles with God:[39] fresh and clean, fun, always. They are the most fundamental manifestation of force. Being squares, like tiny pixels, bubbles of light make up everything. They are literally the building blocks of the universe. What the elements have in common is that they are all built into the fabric of darkness. As matter moves it changes its orientation in relation to a homogenous field (negatively structured by "doesn't matter"), thereby retaining its intrinsic qualities. The mass of the resonance determines the size of its orbit, thus producing its atomic structure. The orbits are all cubic, forming what has the appearance of a shell. The higher the atomic number the larger the orbit, and the greater the heat. All of an atoms' energy (mass) is in the shell. Inside of that is darkness having negative energy. It holds out the light. But now we're getting into Simple Chemistry, which is a whole different subject.

Job 38:24: "Where, now, is the way by which the light distributes itself?" The short answer is booty, by means of an exchange with darkness. But more specifically it bubbles forth. We get a clue to this in the Bible. Psalm 19:2: Knowledge is said to "bubble forth." At Proverbs 18:4, wisdom is likened to "a torrent bubbling forth" (see also Ps. 78:2). 2 Corinthians 4:6 equates knowledge with light. Hence light also bubbles forth. It goes forth by producing a fine foam (not quantum foam) similar to that of a Guinness ale or a fine champagne. The foam moves in every available direction.[40] Light fills the potentialities or crazes around darkness, expanding them and surrounding darkness like liquid envelopes a gas (which you cannot see). Bubbles are lighter than liquid, just as radiant light is lighter than matter. Incidentally, since the bubbles fill crazes in darkness, they are not round but cubic. This is because darkness is like a (really) "fine gauze" (Isa. 40:22). Gauze is checkered (divided into squares).

"Where, now, is the way by which the light distributes itself?" Light is distributed by its interaction with darkness. Darkness is crazed, full of cracks, crazy. Light forces these crazes open and occupies the space or time exposed. These crazes open and provide a space for light to occupy. These cracks are cubic. The light that fills them takes on their shape. The light surrounds the individual details of darkness. The manner in which this occurs may be illustrated with the bubbles of a fine champagne. This is a pressure-driven arrangement. The liquid changes form at the surface creating a foam (liquid filled with tiny bubbles). In our illustration the bubbles represent darkness and the foam (liquid) represents light. The pressure is generated by the light (booty) and the bubbles are always available in the form of darkness. Light changes form when it radiates.

How does light distribute itself? Let's look at our bottle of champagne again. What happens to bubbles that drift to the top of the liquid? They experience a sudden change in pressure and explode in every direction. It is similar with light. In matter, light orbits, forming a bubble of energy. Unseen, like carbonation in a tightly closed soda bottle, these bubbles burst into waves of foam when radiation occurs, being distributed throughout space as radiant energy. The waves could be broken down into square pixels or seen to be digital since that is the shape of the crazes light enters.

The crazes in darkness form cubes. Light occupies these crazes. Light bubbles forth, but the bubbles are square, digital (compare Ps. 8:3 digits). Light produces matter in the form of blocks, cubes, (pixels). These fit together with no wasted space (time). God does not waste time. Blocks are more suitable for building than marbles. I agree. Cubes sound a little crazy, but then God's a little different. He has a cool way of doing things. Oh, and God likes things clean. That's why he doesn't have a bunch of dusty particles floating around, and heaven forbid there should be dog hair (superstrings) in the house. God is the great housekeeper; bubbles are as dirty as he lets it get. And he made this universe big because he doesn't like things cluttered (but not so big he can't keep a handle on it) (Isa. 40:12).

Appendix E

Darkness

Don't be afraid of the dark. Yahowah created it (Isa. 45:7). It is "very good" (Gen. 1:17, 18, 31). Solomon said, "There is more advantage for light than for darkness" (Eccl 2:13), yet both are tools of Yahowah. It's like day versus night. Darkness is simply negative light, the opposite of light. Darkness is serious and still, unlike light which is always bouncing around, moving, happy, funny. Darkness is light's straight man, what light plays off of. Darkness is crazy (full of crazes or cracks), but they're wise cracks. Together, funny and crazy, they are a riot. Humor is the wedding of incongruity and timing. Reality is their marriage. Incongruity (light) and timing (darkness). The same, only different, opposite sides of a pole both lean the same way.

Light works, darkness rests. Yahowah never sleeps (Ps. 12:3, 4). He rests (Gen. 2:2) and works (John 5:17). Darkness, like light, reflects its Creator (Gen 1:4, 5). People don't appreciate darkness. It's like the rests in a piece of music. The rests and "intervals" are not the same as the notes. We don't hear them, yet they add so much to the composition (1 Cor. 14:7). The rests are only perceived relative to those beautiful notes. In the same way, darkness quietly goes about its assigned function, unappreciated. Like the rests, darkness does not vary, but is beautiful in its own right as it supports and complements light. It's time to appreciate darkness for what it is (Isa 45:7).

Appendix F

Relativity

I don't claim to understand relativity, but then relatively few people do—understand it that is. There is a relatively greater number of people who claim to understand it. Just don't ask them to explain it. It's like the emperor's new clothes. Everyone says they see them, but only one little boy ("enfante terrible"—def. "one whose startlingly unconventional ideas are a source of embarrassment or dismay to others") is not taken in. One scientist who thought he understood some of relativity was Richard Feynman. He explained what he understood this way:

"The principle of relativity... means, for example, that if a spaceship is drifting along at a uniform speed, all experiments performed in the spaceship and all the phenomena in the spaceship will appear the same as if the ship were not moving, provided, of course, that one does not look outside. That is the meaning of the principle of relativity. This is a simple enough idea..." (*Six Not-So-Easy Pieces* p. 50 paragraph 3).

"The laws of Newton are of the same form in a moving system as in a stationary system, and therefore it is impossible to tell, by watching mechanical experiments, whether the system is moving or not." (*Six Not-So-Easy Pieces* p. 51 paragraph 1).

Einstein lived in a static, still universe.[41] He published his theory of relativity in 1905. It was 20 years later that Edwin Hubble proved there were galaxies beyond our own. Einstein knew the planets moved, but not the stars. He knew nothing of galactic clusters and superclusters, much less the universe as a whole, moving as a megacluster (Oh, wait, I guess we don't know about that either, but we will). Anyway, the edge is the only thing that is truly still. The rest (actually, you could call it "doesn't rest") moves relative to the edge. Like the sand contained in an hourglass, it all moves. If you say any of it is still, you're not appreciating the condition of the universe. There is no such thing as a still system. When Einstein compared the condition of a moving system to a still one, he was really comparing apples to apples. They had the same rules governing because both systems were the same thing, moving. One was not being measured relative to something still. The only still systems are those which contain the universe, (the edge) (Job 38:19, 20) and in a relative sense darkness itself (although it is constantly vibrated by light). In order for an event to be recognized as relative to something, that something must be absolute. Darkness is the only feature of the universe that meets that criteria. This is the principle of absolutivity. Actually, all the principles of physics are reversed with motion. MTVE becomes (-)MTVE, flippancy becomes floppency, light becomes darkness, present becomes past or future. Everything balances out perfectly.

Einstein was comparing apples to apples. They all move, so naturally the laws of physics remain the same. Now a comparison to darkness, something genuinely still, is different. So different that all the laws governing darkness are opposite, (-) MTVE. Absolutely different. So when Feynman said of relativity, "This is a simple enough idea…" it evidently was not quite simple enough. A still system is governed by the opposite laws of a moving system. Simple Physics.

Appendix G

Antistructure

A basic tenet Simple Physics is the existence of a structure throughout space known as "doesn't matter." Well, I have a confession. It's not that simple. In fact the idea of structure in space is one of the most difficult in Simple Physics. But don't worry. Like other concepts, it's simple once you understand it. In order to grasp it, let's begin by looking at structure of matter. Light is not random. To the contrary, there is not any matter that is not structured. Photons move as waves of specific lengths. Light in atoms orbits, and these orbits are of a well-defined nature. Individual atoms, as well as larger bodies of matter, orbit. Asteroids, comets, moons, planets, even the stars themselves, orbit (move elliptically). Galaxies form clusters, which clusters form superclusters, and which superclusters form a megacluster (singular). Since darkness is the opposite of light, what is the opposite of all this intricate, varied and entropy-driven structure? The answer is antistructure. What in the world is antistructure? It is structure by default, structure that consists of nothing, "doesn't matter."

Rather than manifesting the generally free structure of light, antistructure is very rigid and limited, consisting of tiny crazes of time (space), which are fully occupied by light or darkness. The crazes are mere potentialities for time, yet comprise an antistructure that dictates the space which light or darkness may occupy. Light must have a craze to spread out into in order to move. Darkness must have an open craze to expand into, a craze vacated by light. This is the exchange of heat (light) and cold (darkness). It is a process dominated at a subatomic level by a (really) "fine gauze" (Isa. 40:22) of antistructure. I'm trying to explain by all this that antistructure does not really exist. The crazes are fully occupied by either light or darkness. There are no gaps. Doesn't matter is "something nonexistent" (Isa. 41:12), yet it's antistructure influences everything.

It is of the same ilk as antimatter and negative energy. Would you think all these anti, negative nothings could exist without impacting what we perceive as reality? Antistructure is what causes entropy-driven matter to manifest not chaos, but variety. Matter exists in an ocean of darkness (antimatter) fractured by "doesn't matter" (antistructure). Matter, antimatter and "doesn't matter;" shouldn't a decent theory of everything address all three? These fundamental constituents make up basic reality. Throw in time and you have a complete picture of what's going on. Remember, "Faith is …the evident demonstration of realities though not beheld" (Heb. 11:1). I don't foresee ever "beholding" antistructure, but we see the "evident demonstration" of it. I have faith in these "realities… not beheld" because their reality is manifested in creation. It's how reality works, which is what Simple Physics explains. It's the purpose of this little book. Yes, it's different. That's because no one has ever thought of it before. Have fun with it. Reality is there to enjoy.

Note: When this little book refers to invisible structure in space, it is actually referring to antistructure. - Author

Footnotes

1. *Final* p. 267 "Experiments at high-energy accelerators like the super collider may even solve the most important problem facing modern cosmology: the problem of the missing dark matter."

2. *National Geographic* May 2005 p. 115 "Structure—The Invisible Web". "Something out there holds swarms of galaxies together and keeps their stars from flying apart, but scientists still haven't learned what this invisible substance is. Known as dark matter, it gathers to form a colossal cosmic scaffolding."

3. *Insight* vol. 1. p. 35, 36 "Abyss" (see appendix A). The whole of darkness is the equivalent term. (Author's Note)

4. *Insight* vol. 2. p. 253 "Light"/"Light...refer[s] to...the opposite of darkness, literally and figuratively."

5. See illustration p. 1578 New World Translation of the Holy Scriptures with References.

6. *Final* p. 25 "A field like an electric or magnetic field is a sort of stress in space, something like the various sorts of stress that are possible within a solid body, but a field is a stress in space itself. There is one type of field for each species of elementary particle." Darkness is that solid body. There is only one field, a unified field. (Author's Note)

7. Einstein said massive bodies distort space like bowling balls on a rubber sheet. Darkness is that rubber, only it is distorted outward like an inflatable rubber ball. (Author's Note)

8. *Not-So* p. 143 "It is impossible with space and time so intimately mixed to have something happen with time that isn't in some way reflected in space. It is the entire space-

time which is distorted by the presence of matter, and this is more complicated than a change only in time scale."

9. For example, there is green gold, white gold, the ever popular gold gold, even "good" (Gen 2:12) gold. Everything is the same, only different—snowflakes, oak leaves, diamonds, everything. You just need to look closely enough. God appreciates variety. (Author's Note)

10. *Final* p. 23 "Why? Why does light come in individual particles, each with an energy inversely proportional to the wave-length of the light?"

11. *Easy* p. 26 "Another tremendous amalgamation was the discovery of the relation between electricity, magnetism and light, which were found to be different aspects of the same thing, which we today call the electromagnetic field...the question is, of course, is it going to be possible to amalgamate everything, and merely discover that this world represents different aspects of one thing? Nobody knows."

12. *Easy* pp. 107, 109 "But is this such a simple law? What about the machinery of it? All we have done is to describe *how* the earth moves around the sun, but we have not said *what makes it go*. Newton made no hypotheses about this; he was satisfied to find *what* it did without getting into the machinery of it. *No one has since given any machinery*." "There is no explanation of gravitation in terms of other forces at the present time. It is not an aspect of electricity or anything like that, so we have no explanation."

13. *Final* p. 300 "Gravitons have not been detected experimentally, but this is not a surprise; calculations show that they interact so weakly that individual gravitons could not have been detected in any experiment yet performed. Nevertheless, there is no serious doubt of the existence of

gravitons." I guess that makes my doubt funny. (Author's Note)

14. *Awake!* 10/8/89 p. 19 "The Fascinating Force of Gravity" —"Measurements made down a one-and-a-quarter-mile-deep hole boored in the [Greenland] ice seemed to indicate that the force of gravity differed from what was expected. Previous experiments, performed down mine shafts and up television towers, likewise indicated that something mysterious was causing deviations from the predictions of the Newtonian description of gravity."

15. Objects in outer space appear weightless because matter is light (hence of little weight) to begin with. That's one reason they call it light. The open field of space is minimally distorted by massive bodies, and hence it is harder to detect any subsequent repelling in response to that distortion (repelling we measure as weight). Such repelling does however exist. Everything responds to all the field of darkness in proportion to its mass (or the amount of light it contains). Like all matter, planets too are "light." They are not like rocks, but bubbles. (Author's Note)

16. *N.Y. Times* Dec. 27, 2005 "Many of those who care to think about these issues (and many prefer not to) concluded that Einstein's presumption of locality—the idea that physically separated objects are really separate—is wrong."

17. Einstein's famous prediction that light would bend around the sun is simply evidence that darkness is distorted by the sun (and the path of starlight is dictated by that distortion), not that gravity attracts light. Einstein also said massive bodies distort space like bowling balls on a rubber sheet. Darkness is that rubber, only it is distorted outward like an inflatable rubber ball (meant to be fun). Darkness (crazed

by "doesn't matter") gives structure to space. (Author's Note)

18. *Natl. Geo.* May 2005 p. 115 "Structure—the invisible web. Something out there holds swarms of galaxies together and keeps their stars from flying apart, but scientists still haven't learned what this invisible substance is. Known as dark matter, it gathers to form a colossal cosmic scaffolding."

19. *Final* p. 22 "When an atom or molecule absorbs light it jumps from a state of lower energy to one of higher energy (and vice versa when light is emitted)."

20. *Easy* p. 71 "It is important to realize that in physics today, we have no knowledge of what energy is."

21. See appendix D, "Bubbles"

22. *Easy* p. 112 "In the Einstein relativity theory anything which has energy has mass—mass in the sense that it is attracted gravitationally. Even light, which has an energy, has a mass." Remember, Einstein, there is no such thing as attractive gravity. Mass therefore, is the ability of something to distort darkness. What Einstein did get right was the equivalence of energy and mass (he just got the equivalence off by a factor of C^2). (Author's Note)

23. *Easy* p. 26 "The question is, of course, is it going to be possible to amalgamate everything, and merely discover that this world represents different aspects of one thing? Nobody knows..."

24. *Not-So* p. 49 "...We now know that...the mass of a body increases with velocity."

25. *Awake!* 10/8/89 p. 19 "Recently it was established that the electromagnetic force and the weak force are manifestations of an underlying phenomenon—the electroweak interaction—and theories seek to unify the

strong force with these two. Gravity, however, is the odd one out—it does not seem to fit in with the others."

26. For example, use a quartz crystal watch. Here time is kept by vibrating a small crystal of quartz at a particular frequency. The size of the quartz changes the vibration. The smaller the quartz, the more rapid the frequency—the clock runs faster. Smaller clock, faster time. Time itself hasn't changed, the clock measuring it has. (Author's Note)

27. Space near the earth is stretching out. Space itself (positive time) is bigger, so an object that occupies that space is larger. The object, or in this case the clock, possesses more time. An elevated clock is actually smaller. The fact that an elevated clock looks smaller is more than an illusion. It is, in fact, absolutely smaller and keeps less time or runs faster. An independent ruler would confirm that a dime at the ceiling would be smaller than a dime across the floor. The difficulty with confirming this experimentally is to come up with a ruler that is independent of the earth's field. I can't think of an experiment to get around this other than the one using clocks as the rulers of time. (Author's Note)

28. *Not-So* p. 27 "The fact that the laws of physics are not unchanged under a change of scale was discovered by Galileo...he was so impressed with this discovery that he considered it to be as important as the discovery of the laws of motion, because he published them both in the same volume, called, *On Two New Sciences*."

29. *Easy* p. 26 "All we know is that as we go along, we find that we can amalgamate pieces, and then we find some pieces that do not fit, and we keep trying to put the jigsaw puzzle together. Whether there are a finite number of pieces, and whether there is even a border to the puzzle, is of course unknown."

30. *Insight* vol 2 p. 513 "Number, Numeral"/"Twelve...seems to represent a complete, balanced, divinely constituted arrangement."

31. *Insight* vol 2 p. 512 par 2 "Four is a number sometimes expressing universalness or foursquareness in symmetry and form."

32. *Awake!* 6/22/04 p. 11 "In a university commencement address [Richard Feynman] spoke of 'a specific, extra type of integrity.' He said that this included 'bending over backwards to show how you're maybe wrong.' To do so, he said, 'is our responsibility as scientists, certainly to other scientists, and I think to laymen.'"

33. *Natl. Geo.* "Bang" p. 121..."Einstein's gravity waves could at last offer clues to something he tried and failed to develop: a "theory of everything". Physicists are still seeking such a theory—a single explanation for both the large scale force of gravity and the short-range forces inside the atom."

34. *Final* p. 34 ftn "It is misleading to say that the universe is expanding. Because solar systems and galaxies are not expanding, and space itself is not expanding. The galaxies are rushing apart in the way that any cloud of particles will rush apart once they are set in motion away from each other." Red shift of light is an evidence that darkness is distorted by galaxies rather than that they are moving apart. (Author's Note)

35. *Easy* p. 42 "Or <u>are</u> they particles? They live so short a time, they disintegrate almost instantaneously, as soon as they are formed, that we do not know whether they should be considered as new particles, or some kind of "resonance" interaction of a certain definite energy between the... products into which they disintegrate."

36. *Easy* p. 138 "The uncertainty principle "protects" quantum mechanics. Heisenberg recognized that if it were possible to measure the momentum and the position simultaneously with a greater accuracy, the quantum mechanics would collapse. So he proposed that it must be impossible. Then people sat down and tried to figure out ways of doing it, and nobody could figure out a way to measure the position and the momentum of anything—a screen, an electron, a billiard ball, anything—with any greater accuracy. Quantum mechanics maintains it's perilous but accurate existence." Are those the kind of mechanics you want working on your car? (Author's Note)

37. *Easy* p. 36 "One of the consequences is that things which we used to consider as waves also behave like particles, and particles behave like waves; in fact everything behaves the same way. There is no distinction between a wave and a particle."

38. *Easy* p. 39 "We do not today understand these various particles as different aspects of the same thing, and the fact that we have so many unconnected particles is a representation of the fact that we have so much unconnected information without a good theory."

39. *Natl. Geo.* (Sun) p. 16 "Bubbles the size of Texas cover the sun's face...called granules, the short-lived cells of plasma carry heat to the surface through convection, the same way water boils in a pot."

40. Objects in outer space appear weightless because matter is light (hence of light weight) to begin with. That's one reason they call it light. The open field of space is minimally distorted by nearby massive bodies and hence it is harder to detect any subsequent repelling in response to that distortion (repelling we measure as weight). Such repelling

does, however, exist. Everything responds to all the field of space in proportion to it's mass (or the amount of light it contains). Like all matter, planets too are "light." They are not like rocks, but bubbles. (Author's Note)

41. *Natl. Geo.* May 2005 p. 117 "When Einstein announced general relativity in 1915 he could have taken the next step and declared that the universe was in motion, more than a decade before Hubble directly measured cosmic expansion. But at the time, astronomers conceived of the universe as a large collection of stars fixed forever in the void. Einstein accepted this immutable cosmos. Truth be told he liked it. Einstein was often leary of the most radical consequences of his ideas."

References

Awake! 10/8/89 p. 19 "The Facinating Force of Gravity"

Awake! 6/22/04 p. 11 "Where Can You Find Answers?"

National Geographic May 2005 "Beyond the Big Bang" pp. 115-121

National Geographic July 2004 "The Sun—Living with a Stormy Star" pp. 7, 16

"*Six Easy Pieces*" (Easy) Richard P. Feynman

"*Six Not-So-Easy Pieces*" (Not-So) Richard P. Feynman

"*Dreams of a Final Theory*" (Final) Steven Weinberg

"*Insight on the Scriptures*" Watchtower Bible and Tract Society

Glossary

ABSOLUTE ZERO The temperature of darkness, no light. Thankfully not real cold, but cold enough to hurt you. Cannot be achieved since light cannot be totally eliminated (except at the edge).

ABYSS The realm of darkness (Jude 13). An ocean, "the vast watery deep," surrounding us. The realm of nonexistence, of antimatter (see DARKNESS), abyss describes a place where beings, both spirit and human, are consigned. The lake of fire conveys the permanence of such arrangement (see appendix A).

ANTIMATTER The opposite of matter. Darkness, something nonexistent.

ANTISTRUCTURE The opposite of structure. This is the structure that exists within darkness. Whereas the structure of light is free and loose, the structure of darkness is very tight and rigid. Antistructure consists of nothing, like holes in an orderly arrangement, only these are tiny crazes (see DOESN'T MATTER).

APEIRON A Greek word for describing something that is boundless and limitless, "almost infinite in size." That last phrase sounds a little stupid since the abyss and time are apeirons and can be measured with the span of God's hand. Yet the term is still useful to convey vastness.

BASTARDIZATION Something lowered in quality or character, debased. From bastard—something that is of irregular, inferior or dubious origin.

BOOTY Exchange or ransom. The quality of heat, light or matter itself. Booty is constantly pushing against darkness affecting an exchange with cold or darkness. This quality of booty is expressed in the laws of thermodynamics.

COLD Darkness, felt in the absence of light. A quantity that is limited by absolute zero, unlike heat which is an apeiron. The opposite of heat.

COSMIC AWAKENING An apprehension of God's hand in reality.

DARKNESS A "vast, watery ocean" all around us, but the water is still. It is a field transmitting waves of light constantly. Light travels through a matrix of tiny crazes in darkness. Darkness returns the energy of light, by means of an exchange or ransom. Antimatter, the opposite of light.

DETAIL The fundamental unit of darkness. The cubes around which matter is built, and which surround light (matter).

"DOESN'T MATTER" Crazes of the potential for time. "Doesn't matter" is in the arrangement of a "fine gauze" (Isa 40:22). These crazes infiltrate all of darkness (with the exception of the edge). It is by occupying these crazes that light is able to move through darkness. Since "doesn't matter" is merely the potentiality for time, it does not actually exist. It is "something nonexistent"(Isa 41:12). The crazes only exist in the mind of God.

EDGE, THE The boundary (of darkness) (Job 38:20). The limit, where the crazes of darkness end, and light may not pass. The edge backs up to the spirit heavens.

ENERGY E=M (see MASS). The amount of work required to produce distortion in darkness.

FLIPPANCY Disrespectful levity or casualness. The process by which light is recycled at the edge. Flip, turned over.

FLOPPENCY The opposite of flippancy, serious stuff. The conversion of darkness to light, usually within stars.

FUTURE That area of space which will be occupied by matter. At the present, the future does not exist. It is presently occupied by darkness and is therefore nonexistent. It will continue nonexistent as it becomes the present. The present is the only time that exists. The future becomes the present as the present moves. But the future, like the past, never exists; only the present does.

GRAVITY What was once thought to cause things to fall and planets to orbit. A wrong guess by Isaac Newton. Gravity is still a pretty good name for it. Heaviness.

HEAT Light, the presence of light. The opposite of cold.

INNER SPACE The present, occupied and shared by all matter and radiation. Real time.

JEHOVAH A bastardization of the divine name as expressed in the Tetragrammaton (YHWH). Jehovah was used by 12th century catholic monk R. Martini but was apparently the invention of apostate Christians of the 2nd or 3rd century. There was never scriptural authorization to translate the divine name, but some feared it was lost and so used a substitute (see YAHOWAH) (compare 2 Sam 6:2, 6). The name has long served to identify the God of Christendom although it has fallen out of general use—except among Jehovah's Witnesses. Their continued use of the name is a remnant of their ties and origins with Christendom and "Babylon the Great" (Rev 17:5) (see Rev 18:4).

LIGHT Matter, heat, energy, velocity, mass. Along with darkness, the fundamental building block of the universe. Light manifests itself at all wavelengths of the electro-magnetic spectrum, not just those visible. When light has sufficient mass, its wavelength distorts the fabric of darkness to the extent that it becomes an orbit. It then exists as matter rather than radiation. Matter and radiation are interchangeable, both being light.

MANIC Relating to, affected by, or resembling mania.

MANTIC Of, relating to, or having the power of divination; prophetic.

MASS The ability of something to distort darkness.

MATTER Everything that exists, that has the parameters of MTVE, including light. In fact, matter is light. It glows, radiates.

MEGACLUSTER The material universe moving as a whole.

OCKHAM'S RAZOR A rule in science and philosophy stating that entities should not be multiplied needlessly. This rule is interpreted to mean that the simplest of two or more competing theories is preferable and that an explanation for unknown phenomena should first be attempted in terms of what is already known. Also called the Law of Parsimony.

OUTER SPACE Past and future. Occupied by darkness. Nonexistent time.

PAST (see FUTURE) The area of space that has been occupied by matter. The past is occupied by darkness and therefore does not exist. It can only be appreciated relative to the present, which does exist.

PHYSIC A medicine or drug.

PHYSICS The science of matter and energy and the interactions between the two.

Glossary

PRESENT Real time. That area of space that is occupied by light. All light shares the present together. The present is a continuum. It is eternal. The present, like the universe, will never end. Matter moves constantly within the present and we call this movement the measure of time.

SIMPLE Matt 6:22, 23 ftn "sincere; all one way; in focus; generous."

SIMPLE PHYSICS The science of light and darkness and the interactions between the two. A hole new science.

SPACE Nothing. Before an ocean of darkness, before a flash of light. Just a place to put things, including light and darkness. Time; "In the beginning God created the heavens and the earth" (Gen 1:1). Space came first; time, the beginning.

SOPHOMORIC Characterized by naiveté, simpleminded.

SUPERCILIOUS Feeling or showing haughty disdain; proud.

SUPPLANTER Jacob, one who overturns by sometimes devious means (compare 2 Cor. 10:4, 5)

TEMPERATURE The measure of heat or cold in an environment or body. This is determined by the amount of heat (light) or cold (darkness) present. Cold is limited by absolute zero, however the high end of the scale is an apeiron.

TEMPEST IN A TEACUP Idiom. A big to-do about nothing.

TIME Space, nothing, room for everything; measured as the duration of existence. Divided into present, past and future, by the presence of matter (light) and the absence of darkness. Darkness occupies past and future, nonexistent time; matter, present time. The super-dimension (see SPACE—actually, you will never see space, but notice the entry under SPACE).

UNIFIED FIELD The amalgamation of the four fundamental forces of physics into a single force.

UNIVERSE Uni-verse, single poem, unified song (of God)

VELOCITY The rate of change in the position of something relative to darkness. Nothing is still except the edge (darkness pulsates).

YAHOWAH The Hebrew rendering of the divine name (it has a nice symmetry to it). Once thought to be irretrievably lost, it was recently recovered by the *Biblical Archaeology Review* (Watchtower Feb. 1, 1999 pp. 30, 31). Through a study of biblical Hebrew names it was discovered that the divine name was used in various forms. Yah "which is his name" (Ps 68:5), was already known in Hebrew. Other shortened forms, Yo, Yaho and Yahoo were uncovered. God doesn't mind nicknames, so long as they are based on the original, Yahowah. He wants his name to be sanctified (Matt 6:9). Why would anyone want to translate God's name? (see Supplement)

YAHSHUA A Hebrew proper name meaning "Yahowah is salvation" (see YAHOWAH). When translated it no longer maintains its original meaning but comes to mean, "Jehovah is salvation" (see Matt 1:21 ftn). The name Jesus is a bastardization of the Hebrew original. Yahshua prayed to his Father, "...glorify your name" (Jn 12:28). One way we can participate in that glorification is by using the original name of God's son.

Supplement

Jesus read the Bible (Lk 4:16-21). (I hope I'm not going too slow for you.) What Bible did Jesus read? A translation of the Hebrew Scriptures called the Greek Septuagint Version. In that Greek translation one word stood out. It appeared almost 7,000 times in distinctive form; Hebrew, sometimes in red or gold ink or in paleo-Hebrew characters. In any case it remained untranslated in the main text. This, however, was not a simple word, but a name. It originally appeared in Hebrew and like all Hebrew names it had a meaning. It meant, "Living O he causes to become." But what was the name itself? It contains only four letters and hence is given the Greek designation, Tetragrammaton (meaning four letters). The letters are all consonants: YHWH. How can we learn to pronounce the name without knowing the vowels? That is our little puzzle. We already have four integral pieces, the Tetragrammaton. The key to completing the puzzle is to work with the pieces you have (not pieces you don't have). We don't want to be making this up.

Reading the Bible assists us in solving the puzzle of the divine name. Some find a good place to start is the Book of Matthew. If you begin reading in the New World Translation of the Holy Scriptures with References you won't get very far before you find an asterisk on the title "According to Matthew*." The footnote reads, "Matthew... derived from the Hebrew proper name Mat•tith•yah´, meaning "Gift of Jah." "So, Matthew's name in Hebrew contained an abbreviation of the Divine name, Yah. We term such names "theophoric." If we are serious students of God's word we may recall that the term "Jah" only occurs in the King James Version of the Bible, at Ps. 68:4. That reads (N.W.T.), "Sing to God, make melody to his name; raise up [a song] to the one riding through the desert plains as Jah*, which is his name; and jubilate before him."

The last half of the Divine name is trickier to establish. Hebrew poetry doesn't rhyme so we can't derive it by the sound of the words like it. We get a major clue from the name's meaning, "Living o he causes to become." "To become" in Hebrew is "ha wah." Wah corresponds to the final two letters of the Tetragrammaton, wh. That wah is the final syllable was also concluded by an extensive study of Hebrew names by the *Biblical Archeology Review*.

*Footnote: "Hebrew, beYah´, "by Jah." Yah is the first half of the Tetragrammaton, YHWH". So in Hebrew the psalm would read, "As Yah which is His name." But isn't the Tetragrammaton His name?

Yes, and we still want to find that. But God does not mind nicknames so long as they are derived from the Tetragrammaton. Can we be sure Yah is a legitimate shortened form of the Divine name? Consider the popular expression Halleluyah. Does this simply mean, "Praise the Lord"? According to the American Heritage Dictionary: "Hebrew Halleluyah: hallēlu, pl. imperative of hillēl, to praise + Yah, God (short for Yahweh)". So the manufacturers of the word Yahweh (a popular suggestion for the pronunciation of God's name) were right. The first syllable is Yah. And if it pleases the reader he may address God as such. But why be limited to the more poetic forms of address? Why not complete the name? (Author's Note)

As we've seen with Matthew, Bible names are known to contain parts of the Divine name. There were dozens of examples studied, in fact all the instances found in the Bible. Their conclusion? Wah is the last syllable. But are there only two syllables, as found in Yahweh? Not according to the study. The Divine name should read "Yahowah" or "Yahoowah." Now we can fight over the extra "o". To me, that's just a matter of pronunciation, and since I'm the one writing this and I like things simple, we'll go with Yahowah. See how nicely the vowels, a o a, fit between the consonants, YHWH?

But where did that crazy "o" come from? Professor George Buchanan (who headed the study) states, "In no case is the vowel *oo* or *oh* omitted." The "o" was hidden among all those Hebrew names! It just took a careful search by an interested party to find it. But how did the vowels get hidden in the first place? They used to be used every time the Divine name was pronounced. However a religious tradition developed that the Divine name was too sacred for common people to pronounce. The use of the name was not lost, but was hidden from the public. Why do we say it was not entirely lost? (see Exod. 9:16).

Because it was hidden (in plain sight) in copies of the Hebrew scriptures the whole time. What once appeared as the Tetragrammaton began to be "vowel pointed" by the Hebrew scribes (a pattern of dots used to represent each vowel and put above the consonants). Those scribes were still aware of the pronunciation of the Divine name when they began adding their points. What points did they add? The points for Yahowah-aoa. Now one of Satan's more interesting lies was hatched (compare Jn 8:44, 45). The lie? That these were the vowel points for "Adonay" (Hebrew "Lord") rather than the real thing. This was said to remind the readers to say "Adonay" rather than the Divine name. This allowed the Massorettes and others to obey their twisted conscience and not tamper with the holy writings*, yet still keep the ordinary Jew from saying Yahowah. This suited the scribes who were afraid to play with the Divine name before they attempted to kill it. More direct was the approach of the Jesus worshipers, who were keepers of the Christian Greek scriptures as well as the Hebrew Scriptures. It was in their interests

to eliminate the name completely and replace it with
"Kyrios" (Greek) or "Lord." This practice continues to our
day, with two notable exceptions: Jehovah and Yahweh, a
translation and transliteration of God's name.

> *Footnote: In the Dead Sea Scrolls red ink or
> paleo-Hebrew characters are used to write the
> Tetragrammaton. "That this practice signifies a
> deep reverence for the Divine name is almost a
> truism" (Watchtower, 5/1/78 p. 8). The Masorettes,
> who originated vowel pointing, were also known
> for the care with which they handled the text. Their
> very designation means, "Masters of tradition".
> "The Masorettes changed nothing when copying
> Hebrew Bible manuscripts" (Watchtower, 3/15/77
> pg 18) "These were exceedingly scrupulous and not
> only refrained from changing anything, but were
> careful to restore the changes that the Sopherim
> made, in particular restoring the Divine name...
> "(WT.) To maintain the integrity of the Hebrew
> text was viewed as a sacred obligation. Yet, scholars
> would have us believe that when it came to God's
> name, the most sacred trust of all, there was
> tampering. Furthermore, this tampering began in all
> copies from the earliest on down, and consistently.
> This tampering was the replacement of the true
> vowel points of the Tetragrammaton with those for
> Adonay (aoa). This was supposedly the largest fraud
> ever carried out in scribal transmission (yet totally

out of character for the Masorettes). The purpose was to warn against pronouncing the Divine name and to substitute Adonay or Lord. Never mind that the vowels (aoa) were the same as were already being used with the Tetragrammaton—Yahowah. Does it really make sense? Or did the Masorettes really just keep the original vowels pointed to the Tetragammaton? They then lied about the name in what they felt was the people's best interests (insisting they pronounce it Adonay). We call this fraud "The aoa Prerogative".

Yahweh is a fine effort to restore the Divine name in Hebrew. However, its last syllable should contain an "a" as in ha wah (Hebrew for "to become") and as indicated by more recent discoveries in vowel pointing. More significantly the name has an "o" in the middle, which Yahweh is notable lacking. This disqualifies it as a suitable transliteration of God's name.

The word Jehovah is likewise inadequate. In an attempt to translate God's name, Raymundus Martini, a Catholic monk of the Dominican Order in 1270 C.E., saw fit to render the Tetragrammaton in Latin. He changed the YHWH to JHVH, which I'm sure made the Catholic Church happy (to have God's name in a dead language). The first "a" from Yahowah was changed to an "e" for reasons of pronunciation and thus you have Jehovah, as God's name.

That's all well and good until we realize one truth. To translate God's name is the most bold-faced presumption ever foisted on mankind. Why must we translate God's name? Is it somehow inadequate? It was clearly in its original form throughout the Bible translation Yeshua used. It was even transliterated on an ancient stele, the Moabite stone. Translation of the Tetragrammaton has led to the bastardization of God's name, another of Satan's aims. This bastardization is furthered by the translation of the translation. Jehovah is rendered into hundreds of languages to serve the purpose of missionary Bibles. This reminds me of the practice with Baal in ancient Israel. Baal was a false god of the Canaanites. Everywhere he was worshipped he had a different name. For example, Baal of Peor, Baal-Hazor, Bamoth-Baal and so forth. Jehovah's Witnesses have borrowed a name for God from Christendom. They have translated it into hundreds of languages in order to have the name, Jehovah, in their literature. But really Jehovah remains the name of Christendom's God, like Baal of the Canaanites. The Jehovah word has become an idol and a snare to its lovers. Though recently defended in the Watchtower (Feb. 1, 1999, p. 31) as being "not so monstrous" after all, "Jehovah" is still monstrous, nonetheless.

I want to close this supplement with quotations from five Bible verses, but I'm going to restore the original Hebrew name, Yahowah, in each verse.

Zech 14:9 "In that day Yahowah will prove to be one, and his name one."

Zeph 3:9 "For then I shall give to peoples the change to a pure language, in order for them all to call upon the name of Yahowah, in order to serve him shoulder to shoulder."

Mal 3:16 "At that time those in fear of Yahowah spoke with one another, each one with his companion, and Yahowah kept paying attention and listening. And a book of remembrance began to be written up before him for those in fear of Yahowah and for those thinking upon his name."

Micah 4:5 "All the peoples for their part, will walk each one in the name of its God; but we, for our part, shall walk in the name of Yahowah our God to time indefinite, even forever."

Rom 10:13 "for everyone who calls on the name of Yahowah will be saved." (Joel 2:28-32).

The real Divine name Yahowah should never have been translated. It is not a "Bible name in general", nor does it merit the customary treatment of being translated. It is God's name. Yahowah stands alone, untranslatable, holy (Matt 6:9 K.J.V.).

It has been confidently asserted, "The word Jehovah… cannot be supplanted" (Published in "The Divine Name That Will Endure Forever" (1984) from a publication printed in 1882). Why not? Jehovah's Witnesses are the only ones who really use it. My contention is that that could be changed in one day, along with the name Jehovah's Witnesses. Let them take up God's true name for His people, "Yehowah's People" or if you prefer, "The People of Yahowah" (Isa 62:2). While we're at it, we might as well give a new skin to the Watchtower and Awake!. They should be called simply "Light" and "Darkness" (the latter may sound like a bad name, but that's only because darkness has a bad name) (see *Simple Physics*).

Incidentally, my name also has a meaning:

> **James**: "Supplanter" (English for Jacob) (Gen 27:36)
> **Michael**: "Who is like God?"
> **Jacobs**: "Supplanter" (again, this time plural, to denote excellence).

Jacob or "Supplanter" three times. Isn't that a strange coincidence? (2 Cor 10:4, 5). To paraphrase an old song (from over 30 years ago),

> "Sometimes the lights all shinin' on me,
> [Sometimes so bright] I can barely see,
> Lately it occurs to me,
> What a long, strange trip it's been".
> –The Grateful Dead, "Truckin", 1972

Now that we've solved the puzzle of the Divine name (Yahowah is it!), one age-old question remains: "Where's the Party?" (see 2 Sam 6:2, 15, 19; 1 Chron 13:6). This is the "good news of peace" (Eph 6:15) (compare Isa 52:7).

Why argue?... Crazy.

Supplement to the Supplement

It's time to correct the name Jesus. Like the name it is based upon, Jehovah, it is all wrong. The meaning of Jesus is "Jah (Je) Saves," but the name he was given at birth was not only Hebrew but theophoric. Either Yahshua or Yoshua mean "Yahowah is salvation." I prefer the first form as it contains seven letters, the name Yah, and avoids confusion with Joshua. … "There is no other name under heaven that has been given among men by which must get saved" (Acts 4:12). The name Jesus is another invention of Christendom which should be unceremoniously discarded and replaced with the Hebrew original— Yahshua (see Matt. 1:21 ftn).

"This means everlasting life, their taking in knowledge of you, the only true God, and the one you sent forth, Yahshua Christ" (Jn 17:3). Yahshua's prayer in John Chapter 17 shows his father to be the God of oneness, union and love—the same qualities that are reflected in his creation.

"...if we do discover a complete theory, it should in time be understandable in broad principle by everyone, not just a few scientists. Then we shall, all philosophers, scientists, and just ordinary people, be able to take part in the discussion of the question of why it is that we and the universe exist. If we find the answer to that, it would be the ultimate triumph of human reason—for then we would know the mind of God."

—Stephen Hawking,
A Brief History of Time

"When I see your heavens, the works of your fingers, the moon and the stars that you have prepared, what is mortal man that you keep in him in mind, and a son of man that you take care of him?"

—King David,
Ps. 8:3, 4

NOTES, COMMENTS, QUESTIONS

CPSIA information can be obtained
at www.ICGtesting.com
Printed in the USA
FFOW05n0001090615

9 781936 940936